FRANCIS BACON

Philosopher of Industrial
Science

BOOKS IN
THE LIFE OF SCIENCE LIBRARY

THE LIFE OF SCIENCE
*Essays in the History
of Civilization*
BY GEORGE SARTON

VICTORY OVER PAIN
A History of Anesthesia
BY VICTOR ROBINSON

BENJAMIN SILLIMAN
Pathfinder in American Science
BY JOHN F. FULTON
AND ELIZABETH H. THOMSON

SUN, STAND THOU STILL
*The Life and Work of
Copernicus the Astronomer*
BY ANGUS ARMITAGE

THE STORY OF THE SHIP
BY CHARLES E. GIBSON

**SCIENTISTS
AND AMATEURS**
A History of the Royal Society
BY DOROTHY STIMSON

SONS OF SCIENCE
*The Story of the
Smithsonian Institution
and Its Leaders*
BY PAUL H. OEHSER

**JAMES WATT
AND THE HISTORY OF
STEAM POWER**
BY IVOR B. HART

THE ALCHEMISTS
Founders of Modern Chemistry
BY F. SHERWOOD TAYLOR

**EXPLORER OF THE
HUMAN BRAIN**
*The Life of
Santiago Ramón y Cajal*
BY DOROTHY F. CANNON

FRANCIS BACON
*Philosopher
of Industrial Science*
BY BENJAMIN FARRINGTON

GOETHE AS A SCIENTIST
BY RUDOLF MAGNUS

Francis Bacon as Lord Chancellor

FRANCIS BACON

Philosopher of Industrial Science

Benjamin Farrington

To write at leisure what is to be read at leisure does not interest me. My concern is with life and human affairs and all their troubles and difficulties. It is these I wish to improve by true and wholesome thoughts.

—*Francis Bacon: Letter to Casaubon, c. 1609*

HENRY SCHUMAN · NEW YORK

Dedicated

to

The University College of Swansea

which understands

that

The Wisdom of the Ancients

is necessary for

The Advancement of Learning.

Acknowledgments

MY THANKS are due to Lord Verulam for his kind permission to reproduce photographs of the terra-cotta busts of Sir Nicholas and Lady Anne Bacon and Francis as a boy and also the water-color sketch of Sir Nicholas's house at Gorhambury. The photograph of the house is by *Country Life.* I am indebted to the British Museum for the photograph of the print of Bacon as Lord Chancellor, to the National Marine Museum for the photograph of the print of the *Great Harry,* and to Photo-Precision Limited for the photograph of the monument to Francis Bacon in St. Michael's Church, St. Albans.

In the collection of the illustrative material Mrs. Audrey Williams, Director of the Verulamium Museum, St. Albans, gave valued advice and assistance.

To Max Fisch, Robert K. Merton, and Hugh Dick, who read this book in typescript and gave me the benefit of their scholarly criticism, many improvements are due.

Note
on the English renderings of Bacon's Latin writings
used in this book

Most of the versions printed are those that appear in the Spedding and Ellis edition of the *Collected Works*. But I have not hesitated to make such alterations as suited my own taste in translation and have occasionally preferred to make an entirely fresh translation. In the case of writings not translated in the Spedding and Ellis edition, notably *Thoughts and Conclusions* and *The Masculine Birth of Time*, the versions are my own.

B. F.

Contents

I

Bacon's great idea: The transformation by science of the material conditions of life. The background of the idea. Fundamental inventions which had introduced the modern world. Writers who herald the change: Biringuccio, Agricola, Palissy. The first English industrial revolution.

3

II

1561–1594. Home. Cambridge. Paris. The law. Parliament. Early unpublished writings.

19

III

1594–1603. Bacon's unpublished writings. The first edition of the *Essays*. Bacon and Essex. Death of Queen Elizabeth.

37

IV

1603–1609. Accession of James I. Bacon's second publication: *The Advancement of Learning*. More unpublished writings. Marriage. Bacon appointed Solicitor General. The plan of *The Great Instauration* completed. Bacon's third publication: *De Sapientia Veterum*.

57

V

1609–1620. From *The Wisdom of the Ancients* to *The Great Instauration.*   73

VI

Analysis of *The Great Instauration* continued. The *New Logic (Novum Organum),* Book I.   92

VII

Analysis of *The Great Instauration* continued. The *New Logic (Novum Organum),* Book II.   114

VIII

Analysis of *The Great Instauration* concluded. The *Parasceve.* The *List of Particular Enquiries arranged according to Chapters.*   132

IX

What Bacon achieved with the publication of *The Great Instauration.* Bacon and the Bible. Bacon and the Greeks. Bacon and Harvey.   141

X

The downfall of the Lord Chancellor. The literary activity of the last five years. Death. Editors, biographers, and critics.   155

Appendix A

Bacon's description of Solomon's House, from the *New Atlantis.*   179

Appendix B

Notes to the illustrations.   193

Index   197

Illustrations

Francis Bacon as Lord Chancellor   FRONTISPIECE

FACING PAGE

Francis Bacon, aged 12   16

Lady Anne Bacon   17

Sir Nicholas Bacon   48

Sir Nicholas's house at Gorhambury   49

Frontispiece to the original edition of
  The Great Instauration   49

The *Great Harry*   160

The Francis Bacon monument in
  St. Michael's Church, St. Albans   161

FRANCIS BACON

Philosopher of Industrial
Science

I

Bacon's great idea: The transformation by
science of the material conditions of life -
The background of the idea - Fundamental
inventions which had introduced the modern
world - Writers who herald the change: Biringuccio, Agricola, Palissy - The first English
industrial revolution

THE story of Francis Bacon (1561-1626) is that of a life
devoted to a great idea. The idea gripped him as a boy,
grew with the varied experience of his life, and occupied
him on his deathbed. The idea is a commonplace today,
partly realized, partly tarnished, still often misunder-
stood; but in his day it was a novelty. It is simply that
knowledge ought to bear fruit in works, that science ought
to be applicable to industry, that men ought to organize
themselves as a sacred duty to improve and transform the
conditions of life.

3

This idea, great in itself, received such development at his hands that it came in the end to throw light on the course of human history. From the standpoint of his new idea Bacon passed the whole of human culture under review to see why it had borne so little fruit in works and how it could be improved. The books in which he set forth his proposals are among the great things in world literature.

Nor was Bacon's new philosophy of works merely an intellectual notion. It was with him a humanitarian ideal. The advocacy of it brought into play all his qualities both of mind and heart. It colored all his thoughts and found expression not only in his writings but in his private meditations and in his prayers. Our main task will be to trace the development of this idea in his writings. But we shall find a place also for his other interests and the external events of his life.

In the history of science Francis Bacon takes a leading place. He is among the very great. But his contribution was not strictly scientific. He was not the pioneer in any field of research, the revealer of any fresh law of nature, the author of any great new hypothesis. He prided himself on a revolutionary advance in method, but posterity will not allow his claim. His achievement lies elsewhere. His special concern was with the place of science in human life. It is as a philosopher of science that he is great. He was also a pioneer of the history of science, understanding it in a special way. He did not see science only, or even primarily, as a record of opinions; he saw it rather as the record of what those opinions had enabled man to do.

His ambition was to systematize and organize the development and application of natural knowledge on a scale never imagined before. With him this idea carried the sanction of religion. In the first chapter of Genesis he read that when God made man He gave him dominion over all creatures. This, in Bacon's opinion, was what knowledge was for. He despised all knowledge that did not help to restore mankind to this dominion.

The seriousness with which his whole personality was engaged in his endeavor is one of his greatest qualities. That he often proved himself but a clumsy investigator in the various fields he tried to cultivate does not affect his title to renown. It is true that he was not even abreast of the science of his own day in some of its developments. But his vision of what science could do for mankind was incomparably more comprehensive, more penetrating, and more just than that of any contemporary. Nor was this only an intellectual superiority. In challenging men with such earnestness to win power over nature in order to improve the conditions of human life he kindled a new conscience in mankind.

This was not the mood of the ancient or of the medieval world. Neither ancient Greek philosopher nor medieval Schoolman had in mind the possibility of a drastic improvement in the conditions of human life. Philosophy before Francis Bacon was too often a school of resignation. He stirred a fresh hope and made himself the advocate of a new conception of man's place in nature.

Bacon's ambition was to reconstitute man's knowledge of nature in order to apply it to the relief of man's estate. It is in his pursuit of this aim that his claim to remem-

brance lies. In common with others of his time he was
struck by the effects produced on the fortunes of mankind by a few practical inventions. But nobody else in
his day and not many in the three hundred years since
have thought so deeply and so truly about this question
of the influence of inventions on human life. So important
did it seem to him that it became the major concern of
his life to open men's eyes to its significance.

Others besides Bacon were interested in the program
of invention in this age. The reason is not far to seek. In
the later Middle Ages technical inventions had been re-
markably frequent and their cumulative effect was now
such as to raise visions of the possibility of a radical transformation of the conditions of human life. It is this possibility that holds the first place in Bacon's thoughts.

"It is well to observe," he writes, "the force and effect
and consequences of discoveries. These are to be seen no-
where more conspicuously than in those three which were
unknown to the ancients, and of which the origin, though
recent, is obscure; namely, printing, gunpowder, and the
magnet. For these three have changed the whole face and
state of things throughout the world; the first in literature, the second in warfare, the third in navigation;
whence have followed innumerable changes; insomuch
that no empire, no sect, no star seems to have exerted
greater power and influence in human affairs than these
changes." (*Novum Organum*, Aphorism 129.)

There is here a historical judgment of tremendous significance. Men have been wont to attach supreme importance in history to such political events as the conquests
of Alexander the Great or the establishing of the Roman

6

Empire; or to the emergence of new religions and new philosophies; or to possible influences of the planets. But here by his mention of empire, sect, and star Bacon challenges politics, conquest, religion, philosophy to show results comparable to those wrought by a few mechanical discoveries of nameless men.

Convinced of the soundness of this historical judgment, Bacon goes on to speculate on its moral implications for mankind. "It will not be amiss to distinguish the three kinds and as it were grades of ambition in mankind. The first is of those who desire to extend their own power in their native country; which kind is vulgar and degenerate. The second is of those who labour to extend the power of their country and its dominion among men. This certainly has more dignity, though not less covetousness. But if a man endeavour to establish and extend the power and dominion of the human race itself over the universe, his ambition (if ambition it can be called) is without doubt both a more wholesome thing and a more noble than the other two. Now the empire of man over things depends wholly on the arts and sciences. For we cannot command nature except by obeying her." (*Novum Organum*, 129.) The third ambition was that to which Bacon dedicated his life.

Such an empire over things could be won, Bacon thought, only by means of a revolution in man's conception of knowledge. He pleaded for the restoration of what he called "the commerce of the mind with things" (*commercium mentis et rei*). He was convinced that men must consult nature rather than books if they were to make progress in truth. He pointed out that most of the funda-

7

mental inventions had been made in very early times when men had but little learning, and added: "If the truth must be spoken, it was when the rational and dogmatical sciences began that the discovery of useful works came to an end." In earlier and less sophisticated times men had more direct contact with nature. Accordingly Bacon pleaded for the *restoration* of the commerce of the mind with things, and he did not hesitate to describe this as "the most precious of all earthly things."

Bacon has not always been well understood by learned and bookish editors. They fail to realize how simply and sincerely he meant his praise of inventions and how convinced he was that men must learn science from nature, not from books. To understand him better let us consider the three inventions he singled out for praise.

First, then, when Bacon stressed the revolutionary consequences of the invention of the printing press, he was not thinking, as historians of scholarship do, only of the transference from manuscript to printing of the writings of classical antiquity. He did, of course, attach importance to this. Without access to the older literatures such a historical perspective as he had achieved would have been impossible. But his mind was turned to the future rather than the past. More significant for him than the old books were those embodying new knowledge of the kind that he desired. We shall discuss a few of them in a moment.

When he stressed the importance of gunpowder we must suppose him to have in mind, as he habitually had, the political circumstances of his own day. Though Bacon felt in the highest degree the noble ambition to serve all mankind he could not be indifferent to the destiny of his own country. It should be remembered, then, that it was in the reign of Henry VIII (1509-47) that English naval architects began to mount heavy cannon in the body of their fighting ships. It was the novel possibility of discharging a "broadside" through a row of portholes that not only protected Protestant England from the might of Catholic Spain but was, in the lifetime of Francis Bacon, transferring from Spain to England the control of the seas. Similar developments in the use of artillery on land were being made in the Low Countries about the same time by Simon Stevin (1548-1620) in furtherance of a similar historical purpose, the defence of the Netherlands against Spain.

The importance of the third discovery he mentions, the magnet or compass, was that it stood as the symbol of those great voyages of discovery by which the Portuguese, the Spaniards, and the English had opened up for the first time to Europe the knowledge of half the world.

To the sixteenth century these three discoveries—printing, gunpowder, and the compass—were the symbols of what mechanical inventions could effect. But the history of technology was then in its infancy, and though the sixteenth century did not make a bad choice, scholars in the twentieth century would expand and alter the list of epoch-making inventions. The compass by itself would not have been of much use without a change in the whole character of the ship. This change, involving the invention of a true rudder and giving precedence to sails over oars, made possible the voyages of discovery. Transport by land, too, had been revolutionized in the tenth century

9

by the discovery for the first time of an efficient method of harnessing the horse. Gunpowder alone would not have introduced modern artillery had not the application of water power to metallurgy created a new type of forge, which made possible the casting of guns.

The detailed history of these technical developments remained for the future to write. Bacon, however, understood enough about them for his purpose. His originality consists in his sense of the importance of inventions in human history. His immense learning was applied to the historical illumination of this theme. The full force of his philosophy of inventions was very imperfectly grasped by his contemporaries. The appreciation of it requires an informed and enlightened imagination, and its lessons are even now being forced upon humanity by the pressure of events. But its practical bearing was immediately apparent. Among his ardent disciples was the mining engineer Thomas Bushell (1594-1674). When Bushell in 1662 received a parliamentary concession to reopen the Mendip mines, a contemporary writer observes: "The Lord Chancellor Bacon's philosophical theory in mineral discoveries did light the first candle to these and all other mines of like nature." *

Among the books which best indicate the technical revolution that was taking place at this time, the most significant are perhaps those of the Italian Vanoccio Biringuccio and the German Georgius Agricola (1494-1555). These men, both highly skilled in the arts of mining and metallurgy, were pioneers of industrial capitalism. Biringuccio's book, which is called *Pirotechnia*, was

* *Collected Edition of Bacon's Works,* London, 1730, vol. I, p. 150.

published in 1540. It belonged to a very original class of writing, as will immediately be understood when it is mentioned that, although in the hundred years printing had been in existence thirty thousand books had come from the presses, this was the first on metallurgy. Its author was aware of his originality. He boasted of his uniqueness in publishing a book that was not based on other books but was drawn from direct experience of nature.

Biringuccio wrote in his native Italian. Agricola, a German (his name was originally Georg Bauer), was more learned and used Latin. His *De Re Metallica,* which appeared in 1556, is a still more comprehensive treatise on mining and metallurgy.* It is remarkable, among other things, for its hundreds of illustrations of the tools and machines used in the various processes it describes. It was promptly recognized as one of the important books of the age. The French historian Jean Bodin, writing in 1566, claims that in its own sphere it made Aristotle and Pliny look ignorant.

Nor was the book only technical. It developed a vein of philosophy not alien to Bacon's way of thought. It contains an eloquent statement of the significance of the metal industry for human history, which concludes: "If metals were removed from the service of men, gone would be all the means of protecting and maintaining health and supporting a civilized mode of life. Without metals men would live a brutish and wretched life on the level of wild beasts. Back they would go to their acorns

---

* The first English translation was made by Herbert Hoover and his wife, Lou Henry Hoover, and published privately for them by *The Mining Magazine,* London, 1912.

and berries in the woods." Bacon would have found such truths not unworthy of a place in his philosophy.

We might, indeed, be more direct and say that he did find such truths worthy of his consideration. For he was acquainted with the *De Re Metallica*. He refers to it in the Third Book of his *De Augmentis Scientiarum,* recognizing its practical importance and paying a compliment to its merits. Whether he also knew Biringuccio's book is not certain, but it is very likely that he did. It too was one of *the* books of the day. It was brought at once to England by Sir Thomas Smyth, a prominent figure at the court of Elizabeth, and large portions of it were translated and incorporated into two English books just before Bacon was born, as indeed they had been also appropriated by Agricola.

Late in life the mining engineer Bushell repeatedly claimed to have derived his theory of mining from Bacon. J. W. Gough in his carefully documented biography of Bushell (*The Superlative Prodigal,* Bristol, 1932) has doubts about the value of this claim because it was obviously of advantage to Bushell to exploit the name of Francis Bacon. But Bacon did encourage mining and Bushell was his confidential servant and secretary from about his fifteenth year till he was over thirty (1609-1626). The techniques which Bushell claimed that Bacon imparted to him are in no way original. They are those of Biringuccio and Agricola. But there is no reason at all to doubt Bushell's claim that it was from Bacon that he learned the theory of mining contained in their books.

It was inevitable that England should need these books, for England was now embarking on her first industrial revolution, which took place in the hundred years following on the dissolution of the monasteries. In the reign of Henry VIII, which ended in 1547, England was industrially backward. By the reign of Charles I, which ended in 1642, England was leading Europe in mining and heavy industry. The change is said to have been most rapid between 1575 and 1620—that is, between Francis Bacon's fifteenth and sixtieth birthdays. As the prophet of the application of science to industry, Bacon was swimming on the crest of the wave.

But there is also a sense in which he was a voice crying in the wilderness. What he wanted done with system and foresight was happening at haphazard and blindly. What he vaguely hoped might be an act of planned philanthropy under government direction and royal patronage was being carried out by individuals actuated by selfishness and in fulfilment of no plan.

A similar economic transformation, reflected in both its technological and its philosophical literature, occurred in France at this time. Since this was the one foreign country Bacon visited we shall conclude this chapter with a brief mention of it. It is said that, while industrial progress in England at this time consisted chiefly in the multiplication of material conveniences, in France it mainly took the form of improvement in the arts and crafts. Typical of this progress was the career of the potter Bernard Palissy (1510-89). Apprenticed first as a glassmaker he next turned his attention to pottery, and the fervor of his quest for the secret of the famous white enamel which eventually won him royal patronage has become a popular legend. It is said that he had come so near ruin that he was burning his household goods in order to keep his kilns going.

But Palissy was something more than a craftsman. In fact he made striking advances in a variety of different sciences: chemistry, geology, forestry, agriculture. When Francis Bacon, as a youth, was resident at the French court, Palissy, now a famous man, was giving public lectures before distinguished audiences, and it is very likely that Bacon attended some of them. They were novel enough in themselves, but still more novel was the museum of natural objects by which they were illustrated. Of this Palissy says in his *Discours Admirables* (1580): "I can assure you, dear reader, that in a few hours, in the very first day, you will learn more natural philosophy from the objects displayed in this museum than you could in fifty years devoted to the study of the theories of the ancient philosophers." Here is a startling assertion of Bacon's first principle, which he called the most important of all earthly things, the commerce of the mind with things. It has even led to the inference, which is certainly untrue, that Bacon derived the inspiration for his life's work from the French potter and was too proud to acknowledge it.

It is untrue, because he was already possessed by this inspiration when he went to France. But all the same it can be proved, I think, that he knew Palissy. In a famous passage in the *Novum Organum* (Aphorism 81) he writes: "The true and lawful goal of the sciences is simply this, that human life be enriched by new discoveries and powers. The great majority have no feeling for this. Their thoughts never rise above money-making and the routine of their calling. But every now and then it does happen that an exceptionally intelligent and ambitious craftsman applies himself to a new invention and, as a rule, ruins himself in the process." This is a generalization, but it must be based on something. When we remember that Bacon was for a couple of years about the court where Palissy was employed, the very Palissy who has become the most famous example in history of an intelligent and ambitious craftsman who applied himself to a new invention and nearly ruined himself in the process, it is difficult to doubt that the reference is to him. If it be so, it must also be taken as a very high compliment, for Bacon singles out this high-souled workman from the ruck of routine money-makers in a passage which, in its social implications, is unique in his writings. Whomever he had in mind—whether Palissy or some other—he felt himself united with him by a community of feeling which cut across all social barriers. We shall find Bacon fighting for the idea that the philosopher, if he is to create a science fruitful in works, must overcome his contempt for the craftsman. Perhaps Palissy rid him of this prejudice.

We have said that French philosophical literature also reflects the economic situation at this time. René Descartes (1596-1650) is as conscious as Bacon of the need to supplant speculative philosophy by another kind of philosophy capable of application to industrial production. "I believed," he remarks with regard to his discoveries in natural philosophy, "that I could not keep them concealed without greatly sinning against the law which obliges us to procure, as much as lieth in us, the general good of all men. For they have shown me that it is possible to arrive at knowledge which is very useful in life, and that instead of the speculative philosophy which is taught in the schools, a practical philosophy may be found. By means of this, knowing the power and the action of fire, water, air, stars, heavens, and all the other bodies which environ us, as distinctly as we know the various trades and crafts of our artisans, we might in the same way be able to put them to all the uses to which they are proper, and thus make ourselves, as it were, masters and possessors of nature."

In its philosophic outlook and its philanthropic purpose this is quite Baconian. We may imagine it to have been arrived at independently or, as is more likely, to have been derived by Descartes from the study of Bacon's works. In either case it shows how ripe was the situation for the idea which Bacon was trying to promote—the marriage between natural philosophy and industrial production.

In his advocacy of this idea of a marriage between science and industry, Bacon makes it clear that his design was so extensive that he did not think it could succeed unless it should have the good fortune first to be taken up by the King and then to enlist the support of the learned and influential throughout Europe. He was disappointed in this hope, which, indeed, he hardly dared to entertain. He seems to have regarded it as depending on a degree of enlightenment and goodwill which his experience showed him he was not likely to find. But he did not wholly fail. Though he did not live to see it, a good deal was done to carry out his plans. Within a few years of his death men were grouping themselves together in pursuit of some of his aims. In an appendix we

Francis Bacon, aged 12

Lady Anne Bacon

print the description of Solomon's House from the *New Atlantis*. It is Bacon's fullest and clearest expression of his ideal of organized scientific research. It caught the imagination of his contemporaries. It was in the express hope of making the vision of Solomon's House a reality that Hartlib, friend of Milton and pioneer of agricultural reform, invited the great Bohemian educationalist Comenius (1592-1670) to visit England. And Bacon's project received recognition by the Crown in 1662 when Charles II took a step that Bacon would have liked to see Elizabeth or James take. "The Royal Society of London for Promoting Natural Knowledge" was formally incorporated by Charter. Bacon's great idea, if only in a partial and imperfect form, had found institutional embodiment.

The aim of the Royal Society, namely to promote *natural* knowledge, was a consciously revolutionary step. It was a deliberate effort to substitute observation and experiment for speculation and logical deduction. The novelty of the aim and its connection with Bacon, who had led the attack on the old philosophies, were celebrated by Abraham Cowley, the immensely popular poet of the day, in his *Ode to the Royal Society:*

> From these and all long errors of the way,
> In which our wandering predecessors went,
> And like th'old Hebrews many years did stray
>   In deserts but of small extent,
> Bacon, like Moses, led us forth at last.
>   The barren wilderness he past,
>   Did on the very border stand
>   Of the blest promised land,
> And from the mountain top of his exalted wit,
>   Saw it himself, and shew'd us it.

The same acknowledgment was made in the first history of the Royal Society (1667) by the Bishop of Rochester, Thomas Sprat. "I shall only mention one great man, who had the true imagination of the whole extent of this enterprise, as it is now set on foot; and that is the Lord Bacon; in whose books there are everywhere scattered the best arguments that can be produced for the defence of the experimental philosophy, and the best directions that are needful to promote it: all of which he has already adorned with so much art, that if my desires could have prevailed with some excellent friends of mine, who engaged me to this work, there should have been no other Preface to the History of the Royal Society but some of his writings."

The Royal Society may justly be said to constitute the greatest memorial to Francis Bacon.

II

Home - Cambridge - Paris - The law - Parliament - Early unpublished writings

1 5 6 1 - 1 5 9 4

FRANCIS BACON, the exponent of a new philosophy, was born into a new world. England had detached herself from feudal Europe and was becoming a nation-state with a national church. Henry VIII's distribution of the monastic lands was part of an antipapal, anticlerical reform. Carried out by the lay power of Parliament, it transferred a great part of property in land from clerical to lay control. This increase in the power of the laity at the expense of the church was reflected in the administration. The great offices of state were taken out of the hands of churchmen and given to a new class of lay statesmen.

Nicholas Bacon (1510-79), the father of Francis, was one of these new lay Ministers of State. His father, some

say, had been a bailiff to the monks at the great abbey of
Bury St. Edmunds. He gave Nicholas the chance to go to
Cambridge, study law, and enter politics. After the dissolution of the monasteries Nicholas purchased the lordship
of several of the manors belonging to the abbey where his
father had been bailiff. The Bacons, it may be said, had
no existence except as part of the new order of things.

A few years before Francis was born Sir Nicholas had
become Lord Keeper of the Great Seal of England. When
in town he lived at York House in the Strand, a locality
which then deserved its name, for it was not yet a street
and no rows of houses separated it from the banks of the
Thames. There Francis was born. His mother was Anne,
daughter of Sir Anthony Cook. She was second wife to
Sir Nicholas and bore him two sons: Anthony, the elder
by two years, and Francis, who first saw the light on the
22d of January, 1561. The mother was one of three sisters
famous for their scholarship. Latin, Greek, and Hebrew
were their specialties. Perhaps Anne did not know Hebrew,
but she could write a letter in Greek; and in 1564, when
Francis was three years old, appeared her translation into
English of Bishop Jewel's Latin *Apologia,* the then famous
Defence of the English Church.

Anne was to become a somewhat formidable mother,
but it is likely that at first she made a happy home. Sir
Nicholas at least seems to have thought so. There survive
in manuscript verses he wrote to her about 1557 when she
had nursed him through a long illness: *

* The spelling has been modernized and some obscure lines have been
omitted.

20

Calling to mind, my wife most dear,
How oft you have in sorrows sad
With words full wise and pleasant cheer
My drooping looks turned into glad;
Thinking also with how good will
The idle times which irksome be
You have made short with your good skill
In reading pleasant things to me,
Whereof profit we both did see,
As witness can, if they would speak,
Both your Tully and my Seneck;
Seeing also daily at eye
In my sickness both great and long
Your care of mind and of bodý,
Seeking all ways to make me strong:
I must needs say, and with good heart,
You have well played a good wife's part.

We seem to learn a lot from these verses. There is the active husband impatient of enforced idleness; the cheerful wife capable of refreshing both mind and body; the learned atmosphere in which the wife and husband dispute the rival merits of Cicero and Seneca; the impulse to write, the husband turning his own sentiments into English rhyme, while the wife turns the bishop's Latin arguments into English prose. It was an appropriate home to be born into for the future master of eloquence in Latin and in English.

We partly know and partly may conjecture something more about Anne Bacon. It was in the England of Elizabeth, with the first generation of fervent Protestants, that the habit of family worship established itself. Religion tended to become rooted in the home in preference to the

place of public worship and to consist rather in the spirit
in which the daily routine was performed than in sacraments. Anne was a Calvinist in theology and a Puritan in
morals. We may be sure that there were Bible reading and
family worship in her home. It is often hard for such a
mother to let her sons grow up. Anne's family affection and
religious feeling easily passed over into interference and
bigotry. As Anthony and Francis left the family circle she
followed them into the world with strained anxiety lest
public business or private friendship should carry them
into associations she could not approve. Censoriousness
tends to drown affection in her letters. To Anthony when
he was now over thirty, on hearing both that he was ill and
that he employed on public business a confidential servant
whose religion was suspect, she writes: "I can hardly say
whether your gout or his company were the worse tidings."
There is also a postscript: "I trust you, with your servants,
use prayer twice in a day, having been where reformation
is. [Public business had taken Anthony to Geneva.] Omit it
not for any. Your brother is too negligent therein."

Anthony and Francis shared rooms in Gray's Inn, and
such letters were now a regular feature of their lives. But
love survived these strains. Anne lived to be an old woman,
over eighty. The evidence suggests that both faculties and
character deteriorated in old age. She died in August 1610,
when Anthony was dead and Francis was forty-nine. A
letter from Francis to a friend gives us his mood at the
time. It is to Sir Michael Hicks:

It is but a wish and not any ways to desire it to your
trouble. But I heartily wish I had your company here at

my mother's funeral which I purpose on Thursday next in the forenoon. I dare promise you a good sermon to be made by Mr. Fenton the preacher of Gray's Inn; for he never maketh other. Feast I make none. But if I mought have your company for two or three days at my house I should pass over this mournful occasion with more comfort.

The reserve and the tenderness of this are characteristic.

When Francis was still a boy his father took him to court. He became a favorite of the Queen. Elizabeth delighted in the precocious wisdom with which he replied to her questions and would call him the Young Lord Keeper. What other career could there be for him than that he should go to Cambridge, his father's university? Oxford retained more of the venerable feudal atmosphere. It was at Cambridge that the lay Protestant officers of State were trained. Francis was entered at Trinity College in April 1573. Young men went early to college in those days. Still it may be doubted if he would have got there at twelve if his home had not fostered an early maturity. He was to arrive at a momentous decision in college. All the more impressive is it to remember that, when his studies terminated at Christmas 1575, he was a month short of fifteen.

Of the decision he took at college Dr. William Rawley, his private secretary, who has left us a brief and memorable biography of his employer, gives us the following account: "Whilst he was commorant in the university, about sixteen years of age, as his lordship hath been pleased to impart unto myself, he first fell into the dislike of the philosophy of Aristotle: not for the worthlessness of the author, to whom he would ever ascribe all high attributes, but for the unfruitfulness of the way; being a philosophy, (as his lordship used to say) only strong for disputations and contentions, but barren of the production of works for the benefit of the life of man; in which mind he continued to his dying day."

Commenting on this report, Spedding, who is Bacon's best biographer, says: "I believe it ought to be regarded as the most important event of his life; the event which had a greater influence than any other upon his character and future course."

What is so remarkable about this conclusion of Bacon's? That he came to it so young? Hardly that. Examples of precocity are numerous. That he took a distaste for a particular author or a certain type of study? Many a young man has cried with Shelley:

> But nothing that my masters knew or taught
> I care to learn.

No. The remarkable thing is not the fact that he early took a dislike for Aristotle, but the reason he gave for it and the permanence of his conviction. He rejected the type of philosophy for which the name of Aristotle was the symbol as "barren of the production of works for the benefit of the life of man." He had no quarrel with the system except its practical uselessness. Young though he was, it is clear that he had come to the university with the idea that the serious thing in life was to increase mastery over nature with a view to the improvement of human life.

The expectations which Francis Bacon carried with

him to college can only have come from the influences of
his home, which itself was typical of the age. To understand the boy we have to look again at his Anglican father
and Calvinist mother. There can be no question, I suppose, that the family, made though it had been by the
distribution of monastic lands, did not regard itself as
living on plunder. It would have felt, as many a family
did, that the monks had been idle and that their lands
were now under the more profitable control of improving
landlords. The basis of this prosperity was the reform of
religion.

We have included among our illustrations one showing
the house that Nicholas Bacon built at Gorhambury when
Francis was a boy. Over the fireplace in the dining hall
Nicholas, the improving landlord, had a painting executed showing the goddess Ceres introducing the sowing
of grain. This concern of the father with the great invention on which civilization rests sank into the son's mind.
The first revolution in man's earthly destiny brought
about by the invention of agriculture became the symbol
for him of the second revolution to be brought about by
the application of science to industry. This point is for-
cibly made towards the end of the First Book of the
Novum Organum (Aphorism 129). In his father's hall the
legend beneath the picture of Ceres was *Moniti Meliora*
(instruction brings progress). It was a sound insight that
led Blackbourne, the first editor of a collected edition of
Bacon's works, to add this motto to the frontispiece of
The Great Instauration, in the space where the printer's
name had stood in the first edition. This is the form of

25

the frontispiece we have chosen to reproduce; it is a true statement of the debt of Francis Bacon to his father. The boy whose eyes had rested during dinner on the picture of Ceres became the man who justified his new philosophy of works by appeal to the agricultural revolution. "Discoveries are as it were new creations, and imitations of God's works. Well sang the poet:

> To man's frail race great Athens long ago
> First gave the seed whence waving harvests grow,
> And *re-created* all our life below." *

We must remember, too, that this was just the time when wealth, from whatever source it came—distribution of monastic lands, plunder of the treasure ships of Spain, or the new and lucrative trade in black slaves—was being invested in industry. Mining, metallurgy, textiles, brewing, sugar-refining, and the making of soap, alum, glass, and salt were rapidly expanding. These were the new activities of the new England for the carrying out of which the new knowledge to be found in such writings as those of Biringuccio, Agricola, and Palissy was so eagerly sought after. An eager and precocious boy takes the spirit of the world in which he lives. One may speculate whether Sir Nicholas's library did not contain Richard Eden's *The Decades of the New World* (1555) which translated the first three chapters of *Pirotechnia*, or Peter Whitehorn's *Certain Waies for the ordering of Souldiers in battelray* (1560) which borrows from the same source (though without acknowledgment) all that the age had to teach on mines, bombs, military fireworks, saltpeter,

* Lucretius vi, 1-3.

and gunpowder. But whether this be so or no, it is not speculation but history that from his boyhood Francis Bacon was fired with enthusiasm for the new world of industry.

Accordingly when he went to college and was set to study the logic and metaphysic of Aristotle and the theology of St. Thomas he suffered an inevitable disillusionment. Greek and medieval philosophy had discussed with wonderful subtlety all the possible meanings of the verb "to be" and had logically classified all the forms of existence they recognized. Nothing more could be done with the notions of Substance and Accident, Necessary Being and Contingent Being, Actuality and Potentiality, Matter and Form, Efficient and Final Cause. But now the industrial revolution was at hand. Men wanted to extract minerals from the earth and adapt them to different uses. Here the old logic could not give any help, and Biringuccio could. He really knew how to get minerals out of the earth, how to smelt and refine metals and turn them into church bells or cannon as required. The philosophy of works had already an irresistible appeal for Bacon and he reacted violently against the philosophy of words.

The debate between the respective claims of the contemplative and the active life is an old one and runs through the history both of pagan philosophy and Christian theology. The preference of Francis Bacon for the latter was fed from many sources but undoubtedly owed something to the Calvinistic atmosphere in which he was brought up. The interesting fact, revealed by R. K. Merton in his extensive inquiry into the social relations of

science in seventeenth-century England, of the decided
preponderance of Puritans among the original members
of the Royal Society, gives statistical support to the impression produced by the literature of the age.

No doubt John Calvin (1509-64) was, to his own consciousness, primarily a theologian. But when he undertook to establish a working model of reformed Christianity
at Geneva, he found himself involved in every aspect of
human life. From the reform of doctrine and church
discipline he was led on to the reform of state institutions
and private morals. He wore himself out in unremitting
struggle with the details of the administration of law,
police, economy, education, trade, and manufacture. His
adherents were principally those who had left feudalism
behind and moved on into the industrial epoch. What
eventually survived of all his mass of regulations was what
best adapted the Christian life to the changed conditions.

One of the books popular in England when Francis
Bacon was a boy was *The Laws and Statutes of Geneva*.
It guided the agitation of the Calvinist reformers. Bishop
Jewel was one of those churchmen who had gone abroad
to avoid the persecution of Protestants under Queen
Mary and had returned to spread Calvinist influence in
the Church of England. We have already seen from her
private letters how zealous Anne Bacon was in this cause,
to which her translation of Bishop Jewel's *Apologia* was
a public service. But we cannot doubt that she was
equally zealous in carrying the same spirit into the home.
The general influence that radiated from Geneva was the
sanctification of the secular life. It was not sacraments
that mattered so much as work done in the right spirit.

This mood has found classic expression in the poetry of George Herbert. His poem *Elixir* is famous:

> Teach me, my God and King,
>   In all things Thee to see,
> And what I do in anything,
>   To do it as for Thee.
>
> All may of Thee partake:
>   Nothing can be so mean
> Which with this tincture: "For Thy sake,"
>   Will not grow bright and clean.
>
> The servant with this clause
>   Makes drudgery divine;
> Who sweeps a room as for Thy laws
>   Makes that and the action fine.

Bacon showed no inclination to Calvinist theology. But we may be sure that his early enthusiasm for the philosophy of works, which for him carried with it to the end of his life the sanction of religion, was a natural product of a Calvinistically-inclined Anglican household, in which the father was an improving landlord and a high Minister of State, at the dawn of the first industrial revolution.

Francis Bacon himself was always insistent that his philosophy was to be regarded not as the product of his individual wit, but as the product of his age. Accordingly, when he first formulated his ideas in writing he entitled his composition *The Greatest Birth of Time* (*Temporis Partus Maximus*). This writing is lost, but the title, which is both modest and ambitious, makes clear his consciousness of his debt to the character of the world into which he had been born. His ambition was to voice the needs and aspirations of his time.

29

We have now described the idea which had taken possession of Bacon's mind before he was fourteen. Most of his life was to pass before he gave it final shape in *The Great Instauration,* his most famous work. This was not published till 1620, and even then was only a fragment. But, as we shall see, his idea never left him. It was only as his papers were gradually made public after his death, and especially when a succession of editors and commentators had toiled over them in the nineteenth century, that the extent of his preoccupation with it became clear.

On leaving the university Bacon betook himself to the study of law. He was admitted to Gray's Inn on June 27, 1575. Before he had completed his studies, however, came his first and last opportunity for foreign travel. He was sent to France in the suite of the English ambassador, Sir Amias Paulet, and passed the next two and a half years residing in Paris or traveling in the provinces. Paris impressed him. More than thirty years later, casting about him, as his habit was, for the best way in which to give his great idea to the world, he presented it in one of his writings * in the form of an imaginary address delivered by a philosopher to an assembly of sages. The most impressive setting he could imagine for this address was Paris.

In Paris, and in the provincial capitals of France at this time, a new type of learned men had come into existence among whom the new ideas circulated. Scholasticism had originated in the monastery and had flourished in the university. The ideas out of which the scientific move-

* *Redargutio Philosophiarum* (Refutation of Philosophies), 1608.

ment was to be born circulated in a lay public consisting principally of men with legal training and experience of public affairs. The fashion had established itself of regular but informal gatherings for discussion of the latest views. Bacon had, no doubt, been present at such gatherings. The recollection of them survives in the setting he imagined for his philosopher's address. "There were about fifty men present," he writes, "with not a young man among them, but all advanced in years and bearing, every one of them, on his countenance the stamp of dignity and honour. Some of them had held office. Others were senators. There were also distinguished churchmen and eminent persons from almost every rank of society. There were foreigners also from various nations. They chatted familiarly among themselves, but sat in ordered rows as if expecting someone. Not long after came in to them a man of an aspect that was calm and serene, but habituated to the expression of pity." He then expounds, in one of its many trial forms, some leading features of the Baconian philosophy.

From Paris Bacon was summoned in haste in February 1579 by word of his father's death. The news was a blow not only to his affections but to his prospects in life. Nicholas Bacon was sixty-nine, yet his death was sudden and unexpected. The father had failed to make provision for his youngest son. Francis was left poor, a dangerous situation for one bred in comfort, with powerful connections, and with every hope sooner or later of a remunerative post in the public service. He could not believe that his prospects would not promptly mend. Accordingly, while he applied himself to the completion of his law studies, he also borrowed. He was never afterwards out of debt. It was a defect in the ordering of his life which had disastrous consequences for him.

To enable him to carry out his ambition of service to humanity what Bacon felt he needed was some remunerative post in the public service. But though he succeeded at the bar and became a Member of Parliament, no preferment came to him. He acquired prospects, but that did not help. He was promised the clerkship to the Star Chamber at a salary of £1600—when the post should be vacant. It did not become vacant for twenty years. With his usual aptness Bacon said of this expectation that it was "like another man's ground buttailing upon [i.e., adjoining] his house, which might mend his prospect but did not fill his barn."

In a letter, a dignified begging letter, to his uncle Burghley, who was Lord Treasurer, he enumerated several claims to consideration. "I wax somewhat ancient; one and thirty years is a great deal of sand in the hour-glass. . . . I ever bare a mind to serve her Majesty, as a man born under an excellent Sovereign, that deserveth the dedication of all men's abilities. . . . Again, the meanness of my estate doth somewhat move me; for, though I cannot accuse myself that I am either prodigal or slothful, yet my health is not to spend, nor my course to get."

The last claim he advances is of a different order. It is a statement of his philosophical ambitions, the autobiographical element in which, if it failed to interest uncle Burghley, has profoundly interested posterity. "Lastly, I confess that I have as vast contemplative ends, as I have moderate civil ends: for I have taken all knowledge to be my province; and if I could purge it of two sorts of rovers, whereof the one with frivolous disputations, confutations, and verbosities, the other with blind experiments and auricular traditions and impostures, hath committed so many spoils, I hope I should bring in industrious observations, grounded conclusions, and profitable inventions and discoveries; the best state of that province. This, whether it be curiosity, or vain glory, or nature, or (if one take it favourably) *philanthropia,* is so fixed in my mind as it cannot be removed."

How fixed it was in his mind there is other evidence from this time to prove. In one of her grumbling letters to Anthony Lady Bacon says: "I verily think your brother's weak stomach to digest hath been much caused and confirmed by untimely going to bed, and then musing *nescio quid* * when he should sleep." When Francis mused it was generally on one theme, and there is a writing of his from this date, unpublished in his lifetime but found among his papers, which gives us the substance of his thoughts. It is the first extant formulation of what he called in his letter to uncle Burghley his "vast contemplative ends," and, being written at the same time and in very similar phraseology, throws further light upon it. It is called *Mr. Bacon in Praise of Learning.* It was written probably for an entertainment, of the kind known in those days as a "device," organized by her favorite Essex in honor of the Queen's birthday in 1592. I quote a few paragraphs which are the germ of the ideas later fully unfolded in *The Great Instauration.*

* Some nonsense or other.

"Are we the richer by one poor invention by reason of all the learning that hath been these many hundred years? The industry of artificers maketh some small improvement of things invented; and chance sometimes in experimenting maketh us to stumble upon somewhat which is new; but all the disputation of the learned never brought to light one effect of nature before unknown.

"All the philosophy of nature which is now received is either the philosophy of the Grecians or that other of the Alchemists.* That of the Grecians hath the foundation in words, in ostentation, in confutation, in sects, in schools, in disputations. That of the Alchemists hath the foundation in imposture, in auricular traditions and obscurity. The one never faileth to multiply words, and the other ever faileth to multiply gold.

"[Instead of these two rovers we need] the happy match between the mind of man and the nature of things. And what the posterity and issue of so honorable a match may be, it is not hard to consider. Printing, a gross invention; artillery, a thing that lay not far out of the way; the needle, a thing partly known before; what a change have these three made in the world in these times; the one in the state of learning, the other in the state of war, the third in the state of treasure, commodities and navigation. And those, I say, were but stumbled upon and lighted upon by chance. Therefore, no doubt the sovereignty of man lieth hid in knowledge; wherein many things are reserved, which kings with their treasure cannot buy, nor with their force command; their spials and

* These are the two "rovers" of the letter to Lord Burghley.

intelligencers can give no news of them, their seamen and discoverers cannot sail where they grow. Now we govern nature in opinions, but we are thrall unto her in necessity; but if we would be led by her in invention, we should command her in action."

Two years later Lady Bacon was again anxious and grumbling. "I trust," she writes, "they will not mum nor mask nor sinfully revel at Gray's Inn." Revels *were* planned at Gray's Inn for Christmas 1594 and Francis Bacon had a large part in a "device" produced on the occasion. A prince of an imaginary realm was elected and six addresses were offered to him, all of which Bacon wrote. In one of them he seizes the holiday atmosphere to give expression to the serious purpose that lay nearest to his heart.

"I will wish unto your Highness the exercise of the best and purest part of the mind, and the most innocent and meriting conquest, being the conquest of the works of nature. And to this purpose I will commend to your Highness four principal works and monuments of yourself. First, the collecting of a most perfect and general library, wherein whatever the wit of man hath heretofore committed to books of worth, be they ancient or modern, printed or manuscript, European or of the other parts, of one or other language, may be made contributory to your wisdom.

"Next, a spacious, wonderful garden, wherein whatsoever plant the sun of divers climates, out of the earth of divers moulds, either wild or by the culture of man brought forth, may be with that care that appertaineth to the good prospering thereof set and cherished: This garden to be built about with rooms to stable in all rare beasts and to cage in all rare birds; with two lakes adjoining, the one of fresh water the other of salt, for like variety of fishes. And so you may have in small compass a model of universal nature made private.

"The third, a goodly huge cabinet, wherein whatsoever the hand of man by exquisite art or engine hath made rare in stuff, form, or motion; whatsoever singularity change and the shuffle of things hath produced; whatsoever Nature hath wrought in things that want life and may be kept; shall be sorted and included.

"The fourth such a still-house, so furnished with mills, instruments, furnaces, and vessels, as may be a palace fit for a philosopher's stone."

These ideas too were kept in mind and further developed. They form a first draft for Solomon's House in the *New Atlantis*. We have, then, proof enough that Bacon's thoughts ran perpetually on that projected practical reform of philosophy which had first presented itself to him at Cambridge and had now become "so fixed in my mind as it cannot be removed."

III

Bacon's unpublished writings - The first edition
of the Essays - Bacon and Essex - Death of Queen
Elizabeth

1 5 9 4 - 1 6 0 3

THE letter to Lord Burghley and the compositions written
Bacon's mind in his early maturity so far as it was occupied with his private ambition, his great idea. Before we
turn to the consideration of his public career, which begins to be important at this time, we shall do well to
define his idea more clearly and bring it into relation with
the life of his time.

Hegel (1770-1831) said of Bacon, not without a touch
of sarcasm, that he was typical of his countrymen in his
practical concern with actualities rather than with reason.
There is justice in this. Bacon was not a great philosopher

in the traditional sense of the word. In scholarship he would not stand comparison with St. Thomas, whom he derided. His attacks on earlier philosophers are directed to the main point that their teachings bear no fruit. His writings do not disclose that respect for the philosophical tradition to which it is entitled. But in admitting so much we must also insist on the importance and the historical justice of his criticism. It was precisely because of his grasp of actuality that he became the pioneer thinker of a period of revolutionary change in production. It was a great active enterprise that he sought to initiate and to guide. He tells his uncle Burghley that he has vast contemplative ends, but explains at once that the outcome of them should be profitable inventions and discoveries, and somewhat shyly claims the title of philanthropist rather than philosopher.

In the "device" of 1592 he analyzes the problem which confronted his age. The learning of the day, he notes, bore little relation to the productive processes of industry. Some improvements resulted from the practical ingenuity of working men or casual experimentation. But "all the disputation of the learned never brought to light one effect of nature before unknown."

To remedy this situation he suggests in the "device" of 1594 that royal assistance is required. A library of books ancient and modern in all tongues should be collected. There should be botanical gardens and a zoo on the grandest scale, so that the spectacle of vegetable and animal life should be fully accessible to observation. A museum should contain and classify inanimate natural objects and the products of men's ingenuity and skill. A laboratory should be equipped with all materials required for experimental research.

Such was the renewal of knowledge Francis Bacon sought. If we bear in mind its practical character, Bacon's relationship to the science and scientists of his day becomes much more clear. His point of view differs from that of the historians of science who, not being concerned with the practical applications of science, always connect the renewal of knowledge with more theoretical achievements and in particular with the year 1543 in which appeared the book of Copernicus on *The Revolutions of the Heavenly Bodies.* Copernicus (1473-1543) accounted for the phenomena of the heavens by making a rotating earth revolve about the sun, and his theory gradually displaced the older theory of Ptolemy which made the sun revolve about a stationary earth. Bacon, like others in his day, rejected the Copernican hypothesis. There were in fact genuine obstacles to its acceptance which justified hesitation. Mathematically it was an advance on the Ptolemaic system, but until Newton had worked out his laws of motion there were excellent physical reasons for rejecting it. Bacon, in point of fact, made of this situation an argument for trying to advance science along the whole front instead of in one direction. He called the astronomy which depends only on mathematics and does not also take physics into consideration a "stuffed ox," in contrast with "living astronomy," which does include physics. (*De Augmentis,* III, Chapter 4.)

Bacon gets a black mark from the historians of science for his attitude to Copernicus, and of course he was proved wrong. But the question may be raised whether the date of 1543 and the hypothesis of Copernicus are well chosen to mark the renaissance of scientific knowledge. Copernicus revolutionized the Ptolemaic picture of the heavens. But Ptolemy (2d century A.D.) was not only an astronomer but a geographer. He represented the wisdom of antiquity in what he taught about the earth just as much as in what he taught about the heavens. But long before Copernicus challenged the Ptolemaic astronomy the voyages of Prince Henry the Navigator (1391-1460) and his successors had destroyed the Ptolemaic geography. "With all due respect to the renowned Ptolemy," said one of Henry's captains, "we found everything the opposite of what he said." Such remarks about the ancient geographers are a commonplace of the literature of the voyages of discovery.*

Now it is true that the Copernican revolution meant nothing to Bacon. But the geographical revolution was fundamental in his scheme of things. Nor can it be denied that the destruction of the ancient geography, accomplished by new ships, new maps, and new instruments, was a more dramatic, a more decisive, a more certain, and an earlier step in the renewal of knowledge than the Copernican hypothesis. Here Bacon did not hesitate. This achievement was for him the symbol of the break with antiquity, and it is arguable that he rather than the modern historians of science put the emphasis in the right place.

In any case it is clear that his outlook was shaped by the epoch of the great geographical discoveries. We know

* See in this connection *Europe's Discovery of South Africa,* by S. Welch, Juta, Capetown.

that he was familiar with some at least of the Portuguese records of their great voyages, for he comments on the style of their eloquent historian Bishop Osorius. But of course the later achievements of his own countrymen, contemporaneous with his eager youth, would stir his imagination more. It was in August 1573, the year when Bacon as a boy of twelve went first to college, that Sir Francis Drake returned from one of his voyages, the first Englishman to have set eyes on the Pacific. Some years later Elizabeth ordered the preservation of the *Golden Hind* in which he had circumnavigated the globe, so memorable did his achievement seem to his age. In 1576 Sir Martin Frobisher came back from Labrador with samples of "black earth" which it was thought would yield gold. Next year miners and refiners were included in the small company he took with him to explore the resources of Greenland. Sir Walter Raleigh combined the post of Warden of the Stanneries (tin mines) with his role of buccaneer, and during his enforced idleness in the Tower he divided his time between chemical experiments * and his *History of the World,* a combination not without significance for the student of the age.

It was to this world of eager and active enterprise that Bacon belonged. "When I set before me," he writes, "the condition of these times, in which learning seems to have now made her third visitation to men; and when at the same time I attentively behold with what helps and assistances she is provided; as the vivacity and sublimity of

---

* Bacon took note of these experiments, mentioning them in his private notebooks as a good omen for the future reception of his own philosophy of works.

the many wits of this age; the noble monuments of ancient writers, which shine like so many lights before us;
the art of printing, which brings books within reach of
men of all fortunes; the opened bosom of the ocean, and
the world travelled over in every part, whereby multi-
tudes of experiments unknown to the ancients have been
disclosed, and an immense mass added to Natural History
. . . I cannot but be raised to the hope that this period
will far surpass the Greek and Roman in learning." (*De
Augmentis*, VIII, end.)

It is to this practical outlook, again, that we must look
for the explanation of Bacon's double attitude to William
Gilbert (1540-1603), the greatest English scientist of his
age. Bacon was enthusiastic about Gilbert's practical work
on the magnet, but impatient of the cosmological speculations he sought to raise on the narrow foundation of
the phenomenon of magnetism. The compass meant to
Bacon a contribution to opening up the resources of the
globe. But to what purpose was it to add another to the
innumerable universes which speculation for the last two
thousand five hundred years had created out of a minimum of experience and a maximum of wit? Bacon was
really closer to a geographer like Hakluyt than to Gilbert
in his cosmological mood.

Hakluyt (c. 1553-1616) was the one who did most to
open the eyes of his countrymen to the intellectual and
practical significance of the great voyages of discovery.
His career helps us to understand that of Bacon. After
finishing his studies at Oxford his enthusiasm for the revolution in geographical knowledge found expression in
public lectures at which he "shewed both the old imper-

fectly composed and the new lately improved mappes, globes, spheares and other instruments of this art." In 1582 came out his *Divers Voyages touching the Discovery of America*. But, like Bacon, he wrote rather to stimulate action than to satisfy curiosity. His next writing, which did not get printed for nearly three hundred years, nevertheless attained its end. It was a *discourse* written in 1584 *on the new discoveries in the west at the request and direction of the right worshipful Mr. Walter Raleigh*. Its purpose was to advocate English settlement of suitable parts of North America. Hakluyt had the honor of presenting a copy in person to the Queen. His masterpiece, of course, is *The Principal Navigations, Voyages, Traffiques, and Discoveries of the English Nation* (three folio volumes, 1598-1600).

Distant voyages were means to the expansion of the greatness of England. It is not surprising that they won the encouragement and support of the Crown. But Bacon had an ambition beyond the greatness of his own country, an ambition directed to the state of all mankind, the conquest of fresh dominion by the human race over the realm of nature. He too sought to enlist the patronage and support of princes and leaders of men in his design. But the political conditions in which governments could take into consideration the interests of all mankind still lay hundreds of years below the horizon. Such a political condition of humanity is still below our horizon even today though optimism may trust that in the slow revolution of events its rising cannot be long postponed.

So far we have been stressing the fact that Bacon's main concern was with practical inventions and discoveries. But in his letter to his uncle Burghley he claimed to have taken all knowledge to be his province. What is the connection between his practical aims and his thirst for universal knowledge? It lies in the fact that while Bacon thought the wisdom of the learned had taken the wrong turning and become unprofitable he did not think the labors of practical men could supply the deficiencies of the learned. He observed that in his day inventions and discoveries were in fact made by craftsmen. But he observed also that inventions were few, casual, and limited in scope compared with what they might be. The remedy for this was to bring learning into relation with industry and invention. His idea was not to discard the wisdom of the learned but to reform it.

Here Bacon had hit upon something both new and important. The kind of advance he looked for did not so much consist in the refinement of existing arts as in the invention of new ones. His three symbolic innovations—printing, gunpowder, and the needle—had also this significance for him. Printing was not an improved kind of writing. It was an abandonment of one method of book production and the substitution of another. Ancient artillery had depended on the elasticity of twisted ropes. Now the same function was supplied in a more effective way by the introduction of an entirely new principle, the explosive force of gunpowder. The ancients had steered by the stars and introduced many refinements in that art. With the compass one could steer without the stars. These revolutionary changes had been stumbled upon, because they were obvious, "gross" as Bacon called them. But they supplied the pattern of the new advance, the invention of new arts. This path could no longer be pursued by the short-sighted vision of craftsmen. New arts could be devised only by intelligence, by learning, by theory. Science must be applied to industry.

Accordingly, though Bacon's aim was practical, it demanded for its realization a reorganization of science. From this point of view Bacon could, and did, present his great idea as a reform in logic, a new kind of inductive process. The organizing principle of all his vast erudition was the aim of extending, not man's power of argument, but his power of action. But the special character of his enterprise was his insistence that a reform in practice depended on a reform in thought. So sure was he of this that he constantly identified the two processes, insisting that what is successful in practice is true in theory, that progress in power and progress in knowledge are two aspects of the one thing. It is a mistake to confound this attitude with utilitarianism. For Bacon, works were the test of truth; he did not say they had a value above truth. His clearest statement on the point is this: "Truth therefore and utility are here the very same thing: and works themselves are of greater value as pledges of truth than as contributing to the comforts of life." (*Novum Organum*, I, 124.)

This assertion of the identity of theory and practice brought it about that Bacon became one of the pioneers of historical science. Traditional logic was concerned with eternal ideas, the definition of the true essence of things. Bacon concentrated his attention on a process in time. His theme was the history of civilization regarded as man's progress in achieving his promised dominion over nature.

He thus exalted to the central place in history the story of man's physical action on his environment. His major concern was with the cumulative effect produced upon man himself and the planet he inhabits by the ordinary processes of life. Such knowledge of nature as man possessed had been gained in the course of this struggle to subdue her to his ends.

Such were the new perspectives and ambitions which had unfolded themselves to Bacon's view. He had achieved a new reading of history and a new ideal for the future. His deepest meditations were concerned with the possibility of reducing them to a program which could be successfully offered to the consideration of his generation. Meanwhile he had to live, and we must turn now to see how he conducted the business of living. There were great blemishes in his character, as we shall see. But we shall find him, on the whole, such a man as befits the impersonal grandeur of the conception which had now come to dominate his thoughts.

First let us see how he bore himself in the religious controversies of his age. From his father Francis would imbibe as by breathing the desirability, nay the necessity, of a discreet use of State power to curb the violence of religious zeal. And, while the Elizabethan solution prospered, France tore itself to pieces by religious wars. In his essay *Of Unity in Religion* Bacon comments that the spectacle of these wars would have made Lucretius "seven times more Epicure and atheist than he was." He had the deepest admiration for the religious settlement of Elizabeth and should himself be looked upon as one of the formative influences on the new religion of his country. He accepted the supremacy of the State, but detested all forcing of opinion. From his mother he understood the depths of feeling involved in Puritanism, but he could not follow her in her Calvinism and her anti-Roman zeal. He had a friend, Sir Tobie Matthews, who, after some indecision, returned to his allegiance to the Roman Church. Through an epoch which included the excitements aroused by the Gunpowder Plot, Francis Bacon maintained frank and cordial relations with his friend. This tolerant habit was based on conviction early achieved. In 1589, when he was twenty-eight, Bacon drew up for private circulation a pronouncement on the folly of violent controversy. A sentence or two will reveal the spirit which animates it.

"It is more than time," he writes, "that there were an end and surseance made of this immodest and deformed manner of writing lately entertained, whereby matters of religion are handled in the style of the stage. . . . To turn religion into a comedy or a satire; to search and rip up wounds with a laughing countenance; to intermix Scripture and scurrility some time in one sentence; is a thing far from the devout reverence of a Christian, and scant beseeming the honest regard of a sober man. . . . God grant that we may contend with other churches, as the vine with the olive, which beareth best fruit; and not as the brier with the thistle, which of us is most unprofitable." The literary qualities of the writing—the verbal felicity, the strong rhythm, the apt imagery—are not more characteristic of the man than is the mild and lofty temper.

It can be no part of our purpose to follow Bacon

through the details of his parliamentary career or to take sides in those controversies which still seek to range him in political matters with the sheep or the goats. But a glance at his speeches in the year 1601, when he was forty years of age, will reveal to us not only the variety of public business that was brought to his notice but also the vigor of his understanding, the humanity of his feeling, and the wit of his exposition.

On the subject of false weights and measures he says: "I'll tell you, Mr. Speaker, I'll speak out of my own experience that I have learned and observed, having had causes of this nature referred to my report, that this fault of using false weights and measures is grown so intolerable and common, that, if you would build churches, you shall not need for battlements and bells other things than false weights of lead and brass."

On the vexed subject of monopolies he observes: "If any man out of his own wit, industry, or endeavour, find out anything beneficial to the Commonwealth, or bring any new invention which every subject of this kingdom may use; yet in regard of his pains and travail therein, her Majesty is pleased to grant him a privilege to use the same only by himself or his deputies for a certain time: This is one kind of monopoly." The context makes clear that Bacon regards this a reasonable kind.

On the practice of replacing tillage by pasture, that is, men by sheep, he comments: "The old commendation of Italy by the poet is *potens viris atque ubere glaeba* [strong in men and tilth]; and it stands not with the policy of the State that the wealth of the kingdom should be engrossed into a few pasturers' hands."

Sir Nicholas Bacon

Sir Nicholas's house at Gorhambury

Frontispiece to the original edition of *The Great Instauration*

His first publication, which occurred about this time—the slender volume of ten essays published in 1597—gives evidence both of his now mature wisdom and his affectionate nature. The dedication to his "loving and beloved brother" says: "I sometimes wish your infirmities translated upon myself, that her Majesty might have the service of so active and able a mind, and I might be with excuse confined to these contemplations and studies for which I am fittest."

The first essay, *Of Studies,* is only two hundred and fifty words in length. It ought to be read and pondered by all who would understand Bacon. There we learn that "studies teach not their own use, but that is a wisdom without them and above them, won by observation." There further we learn that "Histories make men wise, Poets witty; Mathematics subtle, Natural Philosophy deep; Moral [i.e., ethics] grave, Logic and Rhetoric able to contend." The serious inquirer into Bacon's thought should not fail to note the effects assigned respectively to Logic and Natural Philosophy.

The precept that "studies teach not their own use, but that is a wisdom without them and above them, won by observation" characterizes all the literary output of its author, not least the *Essays,* which remain the best-known and best-liked portion of his work. Reissued with additions in 1612, they eventually (in 1625) reached a total of fifty-eight, many of them of much greater length than any of the first ten. Miscellaneous though their subjects are, they not unfairly represent the true genius of their author, which was to be a philosopher in the popular sense—not of a man who has elaborated a new view of the universe, but of one who is wiser than other men in his judgments on men and affairs. They have been accused of Machiavellism, and it is true that Bacon approved the wisdom of the serpent equally with the innocence of the dove. But they are sown thick with beauty, dignity, and sweetness, which qualities are yet so unaffected that they mix naturally with the homeliest wisdom and the raciest expression. So striking are individual sentences that one is perpetually tempted to quote, yet so close is the texture of the writing that the jewel seems less fair when removed from its setting. In lieu of quotations I shall recommend the reader of this book to read also Essay XXXIII, *Of Plantations.* If the practical wisdom and moral beauty of that essay are to his taste he will not fail to love the man Bacon.

The original volume of ten little essays, which could easily be printed on ten little pages, was published by Bacon himself to forestall unauthorized publication by others. The circumstance is proof of the estimation in which his wisdom was beginning to be held. Among those who had benefited in private by his advice was Robert Devereux, second Earl of Essex, with whom Bacon's friendship was now at its height. Essex was Bacon's junior by some six years. Graduating at Cambridge in 1581, he appeared at Court in 1584, a youth of seventeen years of age. Next year he accompanied Elizabeth's favorite, the Earl of Leicester, on an expedition to Holland and distinguished himself at the battle of Zutphen. A career of military distinction was opening before him when he had the misfortune, as a youth of twenty-one, to succeed the

Earl of Leicester as the favorite of the Queen who was now nearly sixty.

It will be seen that Essex stood in sore need of the advice of an older and wiser friend. His position was difficult in the extreme. Apart from the ups and downs of fortune which it was in the Queen's power to bestow according to the degree of contentment she felt with her courtier, we learn also that Essex had to endure the personal humiliation of face-slapping on an occasion when his self-control broke down and he betrayed his impatience and disgust. Bacon enjoyed material favors from Essex, including the gift of a valuable property. He repaid the favors with advice which, as long as it was attended to, saved Essex from disaster. In the end, however, Essex drifted into treasonable courses, was arraigned, condemned, and executed.

Bacon, by his position as Learned Counsel to the Queen, was involved in the prosecution of his friend. He spoke twice, each time tearing aside a flimsy excuse by which treason was made to appear a more pardonable crime. "I have never yet seen in any case," said Bacon, "such favour shown to any prisoner; so many digressions, such delivering of evidence by fractions, and so silly [i.e., empty] a defence of such great and notorious treasons." Bacon's conduct has by some been very harshly judged. Yet nobody denies that Essex was guilty of treason and it is difficult to understand what those who condemn Bacon would have had him do. Spedding, who spent more time collecting and putting before the public all the available evidence than any other inquirer has done, writes: "In a note to Dr. Rawley's 'Life of Bacon' I said that I had no fault to find with him for any part of his conduct towards Essex. Closer examination has not at all altered my opinion."

I cannot dissent from this opinion. At the trial Bacon protested that "he had spent more time in vain in studying to make the Earl a good servant to the Queen and state, than he had done in anything else." He detailed his grounds for this statement in a defense of his share in the prosecution published in 1604. It is a weighty document the truth of which is not in dispute. It is valuable also as containing a definition of the principle on which Bacon based his conduct in this matter. "My defence needeth to be but simple and brief: namely, that whatsoever I did concerning that action and proceeding, was done in my duty and service to the Queen and State; in which I would not show myself false-hearted nor fainthearted for any man's sake living. For every honest man, that hath his heart well planted, will forsake his King rather than forsake God, and forsake his friend rather than forsake his King; and yet will forsake any earthly commodity, yea and his own life in some cases, rather than forsake his friend."

What is one to quarrel with in Bacon's conduct? His conception of where his duty lay? His ability to perform it? Or the fact that he has not left us some intimate document inviting posterity to share the difficulty and the cruelty of his position?

Essex was executed in 1601. Two years later Elizabeth followed him to the grave, "departing this life mildly, like a lamb; easily, like a ripe apple from the tree," to borrow the expression of a diarist of this golden age of English literature. The change of ruler was for Bacon the occasion for a meditation on his conduct of his life. The accession of James VI of Scotland to the throne of England, and the Union of the Crowns under a sovereign distinguished for his learning, raised new hopes in Bacon of the possibility of his finding a royal ear open to his great design for the improvement of the lot of humanity. But the urge to abandon public life and concentrate on his great reform was also insistent. We shall close this chapter by quoting a document unique among his writings as being the only piece of autobiography in which he indulged.

The form of the document is a Preface to a proposed work *On the Interpretation of Nature,* a work not yet written but largely thought out. It was composed in 1603, obviously at a time when Bacon had decided to give up public life and confine his energies to authorship and prosecution of his great idea. It explains why he had ever consented to a public career instead of devoting all his energies to perfecting the philosophy of works. It was never included in his published writings because the work to which it was designed as a preface was never written in the projected form. Among its many interesting features we may single out his sober characterization of his own intellectual qualities. The document was written in Latin. We quote here, from Spedding's admirable version, about half of the whole piece.

"Believing that I was born for the service of mankind, and regarding the care of the commonwealth as a kind of common property which like the air and the water belongs to everybody, I set myself to consider in what

way mankind might best be served, and what service I
was myself by nature best fitted to perform.

"Now among all the benefits that could be conferred
upon mankind, I found none so great as the discovery
of new arts, endowments, and commodities for the bet-
tering of man's life. For I saw that among the rude people
in the primitive times the authors of rude inventions and
discoveries were consecrated and numbered among the
Gods. And it was plain that the good effects wrought
by founders of cities, law-givers, fathers of the people,
extirpers of tyrants, and heroes of that class, extend but
over narrow spaces and last but for short times; whereas
the work of the Inventor, though a thing of less pomp
and show, is felt everywhere and lasts for ever.

"But above all, if a man could succeed, not in striking
out some particular invention, however useful, but in
kindling a light in nature—a light which should in its
very rising touch and illuminate all the border-regions
that confine upon the circle of our present knowledge;
and so spreading further and further should presently
disclose and bring into sight all that is most hidden and
secret in the world,—that man (I thought) would be the
benefactor indeed of the human race,—the propagator
of man's empire over the universe, the champion of lib-
erty, the conqueror and subduer of necessities.

"For myself, I found that I was fitted for nothing so
well as for the study of Truth; as having a mind nimble
and versatile enough to catch the resemblances of things
(which is the chief point), and at the same time steady
enough to fix and distinguish their subtler differences;
as being gifted by nature with desire to seek, patience

to doubt, fondness to meditate, slowness to assert, readiness to reconsider, carefulness to dispose and set in order; and as being a man that neither affects what is new nor admires what is old, and that hates every kind of imposture. So I thought my nature had a kind of familiarity and relationship with Truth.

"Nevertheless, because my birth and education had seasoned me in business of state; and because opinions (so young as I was) would sometimes stagger me; and because I thought that a man's own country has some special claims upon him more than the rest of the world; and because I hoped that, if I rose to any place of honour in the state, I should have a larger command of industry and ability to help me in my work;—for these reasons I both applied myself to acquire the arts of civil life, and commended my service, so far as in modesty and honesty I might, to the favour of such friends as had any influence. In which also I had another motive: for I felt that those things I have spoken of—be they great or small—reach no further than the condition and culture of this mortal life; and I was not without hope (the condition of Religion being at that time not very prosperous) that if I came to hold office in the state, I might get something done too for the good of men's souls.

"When I found however that my zeal was mistaken for ambition, and my life had already reached the turning-point, and my breaking health reminded me how ill I could afford to be slow, and I reflected moreover that in leaving undone that good I could do by myself alone, and applying myself to that which could not be done without the help and consent of others, I was by no means discharging the duty that lay upon me,—I put all those thoughts aside, and (in pursuance of my old determination) betook myself wholly to this work."

With this quotation we may fitly conclude a chapter the main purpose of which has been to fix in our minds the outline of the moral character of the author of *The Great Instauration.*

IV

Accession of James I - Bacon's second publication: *The Advancement of Learning* - More unpublished writings - Marriage - Bacon appointed Solicitor-General - The plan of *The Great Instauration* completed - Bacon's third publication: *De Sapientia Veterum*

1603 - 1609

Bacon's career under Elizabeth had been one long disappointment. He had looked for preferment and had not got it. In 1589, as we have said, he had secured the reversion of the clerkship of the Star Chamber, but the post did not become vacant for twenty years. A few years later he suffered a double rebuff. He aspired to the attorney-generalship but in March 1594 saw Coke appointed to it. This left the solicitor-generalship vacant, but even this lesser post was denied to Bacon. It went to Sergeant

Thomas Fleming in October of 1595. It was then that
Essex generously insisted on compensating his friend and
mentor by the gift of a piece of land near Twickenham
Park. But, of course, an estate worth £1800 was no substitute for an annual income of about the same amount,
which was more nearly what Bacon needed.

By the time of James's accession it is no wonder that
Bacon had in mind to drop his public career and apply
himself to his writing. He still sought the backing of the
King. But what he wanted from the King was not office
but support for his projected reform of philosophy. James
was himself learned and might be expected to be a patron
of learning. But there could be no guarantee that a king
so proud of his traditional learning as to be somewhat of
a pedant would be in the least interested in a proposal
to create a new kind of philosophy to supersede the old.

What then was Bacon to do? His works from this period, published and unpublished, reveal his difficulty and
the way he sought to surmount it. In order to interest the
King and, no doubt, also to establish his reputation—for
as yet, though he was forty-two years old he had published nothing but his ten little *Essays*—he resolved on
the composition of a work sufficiently conventional to
secure approval and sufficiently close to his grand design
as to prepare the way for it. The outcome of this line of
thought was the two books of *The Advancement of Learning,* published in October 1605 and dedicated to the King.
The first treats of the excellence and dignity of knowledge as a pursuit for kings and statesmen. The second
seeks to indicate the deficiencies of existing knowledge
and to suggest how they might be supplied. With the

contents of the former we are already in large part familiar, for it gathered together many of the thoughts
which we have already met in his unpublished writings.
But since the book is one of the most brilliant and carefully wrought of his compositions in English it is desirable to quote something from it. We choose the famous
passage in which he attacks Scholasticism for its scarcity
of facts and superfluity of logic. The passage will be
better understood if the reader will return to it after finishing this book.

"This kind of degenerate learning did chiefly reign
among the schoolmen: who having sharp and strong
wits, and abundance of leisure, and small variety of reading, (but their wits being shut up in the cells of a few
authors, chiefly Aristotle their dictator, as their persons
were shut up in the cells of monasteries and colleges),
and knowing little history, either of nature or time, did,
out of no great quantity of matter, and infinite agitation
of wit, spin out unto us those laborious webs of learning,
which are extant in their books. For the wit and mind
of man, if it work upon matter, which is the contemplation of the creatures of God, worketh according to the
stuff, and is limited thereby; but if it work upon itself,
as the spider worketh his web, then it is endless, and
brings forth indeed cobwebs of learning, admirable for
the fineness of thread and work, but of no substance or
profit."

Of the second book of *The Advancement of Learning*
we say nothing now. It was later revised, translated into
Latin, and published under the title *De Augmentis Scientiarum*. This was in October 1623, just eighteen years

after its first appearance. We shall discuss it in its place.

The Advancement of Learning was a very remarkable book and is still worth study. It showed that Bacon had made no idle boast when he said that he had taken all learning to be his province. It showed also what he meant when he said that studies do not teach their own use; for the most valuable part of the *Advancement* is the criticism of the limitations of existing knowledge, which is drawn from Bacon's experience of life rather than from his reading. It must never be forgotten that Bacon belonged to that tiny minority of writers who make books out of life, not to the immense majority who make books out of books.

Nevertheless the *Advancement* did not, and in the existing circumstances could not, contain the most important lesson Bacon had learned from life. The conviction that all knowledge had gone astray because it was not based on the commerce of the mind with things, and that nothing short of an entirely fresh start could remedy the ill, would not have been listened to either by James or by the English reading public. Bacon had now been nursing this idea in his mind for some thirty years and had found by experience that it was difficult, if not impossible, to find anyone to share it. It had bitten deep into his consciousness that "it is not a thing so easy as is conceived to convey the conceit of one man's mind into the mind of another without loss or mistaking, specially in notions new and differing from those that are received." (*Valerius Terminus*, Chapter 18.) It had bitten equally deep into his consciousness, as we saw at the end of the last chapter, that he would be guilty of a crime against humanity if he did not carry out the work he believed himself born to perform. Accordingly, in addition to the *Advancement,* which he wrote quickly for publication, he began to experiment in various ways of clothing his idea so that it might win acceptance.

Hence an abundance of writings, mostly in Latin, which often are among the most brilliant, polished, and graceful of his compositions, but which never saw the light till he was dead. True, most of the ideas were gathered up into one or other of the few writings he published in his lifetime. Nevertheless the smaller writings which he left unpublished have an additional interest which is all their own. They have sometimes a peculiar freshness, and they enable us to understand the tireless patience with which he labored to make his idea intelligible to his generation. He did not succeed, nor has posterity completely understood him either.

There are about a dozen writings which might be included in this class. The titles are all in Latin. I give the list with the English first and Latin in parentheses after:

1. Thoughts on the Nature of Things (*Cogitationes de Natura Rerum*).
2. The Mighty Works of Nature (*Magnalia Naturae*).
3. Thoughts on Human Knowledge (*Cogitationes de Humana Scientia*).
4. Valerius Terminus. (The meaning of the mysterious title, which does not concern us here, is best explained in Fulton Anderson's *Philosophy of Francis Bacon,* p. 16.)

5. The Thread of the Labyrinth (*Filum Labyrinthi*). This in spite of the title is in English, and the substance is the same as 9 below.

6. Concerning the Interpretation of Nature: Preface (*De Interpretatione Naturae: Proœmium*). This is the writing quoted at the end of the last chapter.

7. The Masculine Birth of Time (*Temporis Partus Masculus*).

8. Refutation of Philosophies (*Redargutio Philosophiarum*).

9. Thoughts and Conclusions (*Cogitata et Visa*).

10. The Phenomena of the Universe (*Phænomena Universi*).

11. The Description of the Intellectual World (*Descriptio Globi Intellectualis*).

12. Theory of the Heavens (*Thema Coeli*).

Our purpose is not to discuss the contents of all of these, in which there is a good deal of repetition. We shall content ourselves with picking out some of the main topics. But their very number is impressive. We have listed them to facilitate reference and we wish to make clear the intensity of Bacon's effort to attain not only clarity and brilliance but also an acceptable presentation. This can best be done by a glance at these writings.

Of the trouble he took with these unpublished pieces Nos. 8 and 9 are the best proof. They are among the most finished of his writings. Nos. 5 and 9 illustrate another concern. Bacon had always to consider whether he would write for a national audience in English or an international audience in Latin. With a few changes No. 9 is but a Latin version of No. 5. On the question of obtruding his own personality on the reader Bacon soon came to the decision to keep himself in the background as much as possible. No. 6 is, as we have seen, unique in being an autobiographical piece in the first person. Bacon preferred reserve. Nos. 5 and 9 accordingly follow the example of Julius Caesar in his *Commentaries*. Bacon here speaks of himself in the third person: "Francis Bacon thought thus [*Franciscus Baconus sic cogitavit*]." There is something impressive in this unusual convention. Bacon's great admirer, the Neapolitan philosopher Giovanni Battista Vico, adopted it also in his wonderful biography. It has the effect of making the writer's thoughts appear already a part of history.

These examples by no means exhaust Bacon's concern with the problem of style. We accidentally possess some pages of private notes he made at this time. They contain reminders to himself of possible ways of solving the problem of presentation. One of them recommends "taking a greater confidence and authority in discourses of this nature, *tanquam sui certus et de alto despiciens*" (as if sure of himself and looking down from a height). Another goes further in the same direction. It recommends "discoursing scornfully of the philosophy of the Grecians." A third goes in the opposite direction and raises the question of composing "an oration" which should be "delightful" and "sublime," addressed as by an old man to his disciples and written in a moving and appealing way.

It is fascinating to find these hints followed out in some of these unpublished pieces. One, No. 7, shows us Bacon "discoursing scornfully" about the Greeks. No. 9, an exceptionally polished piece, is an oration in a lofty tone expressive rather of sorrow for mankind than scorn for its false prophets. It is in this piece that Bacon seems to recall his youthful visit to France. The setting for the oration is a learned Paris salon.

These two writings contain the sharpest possible attack on Plato and Aristotle. There should be nothing to surprise us in this. Bacon's earliest intimation of his guiding idea involved a revolt from Aristotle. In the most famous of the writings published in his lifetime the attack on Plato and Aristotle is explicit and severe. Nevertheless the language he employs in *The Masculine Birth of Time* has been a cause of scandal.

Aristotle he calls a wretched sophist, his logic a manual of madness, his metaphysics a superstructure of cobwebs erected on a small foundation of fact. His language about Plato is, if anything, stronger. We quote the passage in full. "Let Plato next be summoned to the bar, that witty detractor, that swelling poet, that deluded theologian. Your philosophy, Plato, was but scraps of second-hand information polished and strung together. Your wisdom was a sham which you achieved by an affectation of ignorance. You tempted the minds of men by vague inductions, but were never able to bring them beyond these uncertainties. But at least you had the merit of supplying topics for the table-talk of men of culture and experience, even indeed of adding grace and charm to every-day conversation. When, however, you falsely asserted that truth is, as it were, the native inhabitant of the human mind and does not come from outside in order to take up its abode there; when you turned our minds away from ob-

64

servation and away from things, to which it is impossible
that they should ever be sufficiently attentive and obe-
dient; when you taught us to turn our minds inward and
grovel before our own blind and confused idols under
the name of contemplative philosophy; then truly you
dealt us a mortal injury. It should not be forgotten either
that you were guilty of a hardly lesser sin when you dei-
fied your folly and presumed to shore up your contemptible thoughts with the prop of religion."

It has been the custom of editors, when they allude
at all to these attacks, to suggest that they were not seriously intended. To show that Bacon did not mean them
they quote from the *Refutation of Philosophies*. Here Bacon says of Plato and Aristotle: "If anybody does not
recognise them as among the greatest minds of humanity
he must be stupid or unjust." But there is no real contradiction here. Bacon intended every word he uttered
against Plato and Aristotle, although he did not give his
final approbation to the deliberately adopted tone of
scorn. He leaves us no room for doubt. At the end of *The
Masculine Birth of Time* he writes: "But now I must rec-
ollect myself and do penance for, even though my purpose was to discredit it, yet I have been handling the
unholy and the unclean [*profana et polluta*]. What I have
said against them all [i.e., Plato, Aristotle, and many
others ancient and modern] has been less than their monstrous guilt deserved. You, gentle reader, perhaps do not
understand my confutation of them. Without a doubt you
regard the charges I have levelled against them as mere
abuse. But indeed it is not so. When you have had time
to reflect you will think differently. You will admire be-

neath the veil of abuse the spirit that has animated my attack. You will see with what skill I have packed my meaning into every word and with what deadly accuracy I have launched my shafts straight into their hidden sores. Indeed while those whom I incriminate share one another's guilt and might easily be confounded in a common accusation, I have been at pains to frame an indictment appropriate to each individual and particularising his chief offence."

But this is not all. In the *Refutation of Philosophies*, from which the editors quote Bacon's recognition of the genius of Plato and Aristotle, we find the same charges repeated and expanded, though in a tone appropriate to the deliberately lofty style of that oration. There Bacon assures us that the minds of Plato and Aristotle were "vast, penetrating, and sublime." But this, though certainly sincerely meant, is simply the prelude to a renewal of the attack launched in *The Masculine Birth of Time*, an attack all the more impressive as being now delivered in a tone of quiet earnestness and with a more leisurely expansion of the various points. Instead of calling Aristotle "a sophist" there is now a paragraph devoted to the justification of the charge. Instead of calling Plato "a swelling poet" it is now argued that he had no real interest in natural philosophy but acquired only so much of it as was necessary to add majesty to his ethical and political writings. Here we find the justification of the previous claim that beneath the veil of scornful abuse would be found a careful weighing of his words. The final judgment is that "Plato corrupted natural philosophy by his theology as thoroughly as Aristotle by his logic."

It is therefore idle to pretend that Bacon had a profound admiration for the philosophy of Aristotle and Plato, although he did admire the men themselves. As we shall see later when we come to discuss the *Novum Organum,* he considered the survival of their works merely a proof of their superficiality. It is not our purpose to argue that Bacon's judgment is adequate, but we must be clear what his judgment was. Here there is no room for doubt. He regarded them both as men of outstanding mental gifts who had produced mischievous systems of thought. Any comprehension of Bacon is impossible unless it is realized that he regarded the influence of Plato and Aristotle as the chief obstacle to the foundation of a true philosophy of nature.

Bacon's position is, however, crystal clear. "There is," he says, "a powerful cause why the sciences have made but little progress. It is not possible to run a course rightly when the goal itself has been wrongly set. Now the true and lawful goal of the sciences is simply this, that human life be endowed with new discoveries and powers." Aristotle in the first book of his *Metaphysics* makes it clear that he regards this process as finished. He says explicitly that all the necessities and refinements of life have already been invented. Plato's position is implicitly the same. But, according to Bacon, this opinion spelled the doom, not only of the material, but also of the mental, progress of mankind.

In his *Thoughts and Conclusions* Bacon writes: "If there be any one on whose ear my frequent praise of practical activities has a harsh and unpleasing sound because he is wholly devoted to contemplative philosophy, let me assure him that he is the enemy of his own desires. In natural philosophy practical results are not only the means to improve human well-being. They are also the guarantee of truth. There is a true rule in religion, that a man must show his faith by his works. The same rule holds good in natural philosophy. Science too must be known by its works. It is by the witness of works rather than by logic or even observation that truth is revealed and established. It follows from this that the improvement of man's lot and the improvement of man's mind are one and the same thing."

Now Bacon urged that with Plato and Aristotle the goal was wrongly set and that, in consequence of this, though they were among the most brilliant geniuses known to history their philosophy was valueless. In his *Thoughts and Conclusions* he writes again, with reference to these and other philosophers: "When we reject their conclusions, it must be understood that we are attacking only their opinions, not their genius nor their exertions. In fact the more brilliant and industrious a man is, if he neglects the light supplied by nature, abandons research, and turns his back on the evidence of facts, he only loses himself the more thoroughly in the labyrinth of his own imagination."

The whole history of philosophy seemed to Bacon to be a sort of wandering in the wilderness. That was the meaning of Abraham Cowley's verse quoted in our first chapter. But Bacon also saw—and was perhaps the first to do so—that, whereas philosophy is stationary, applied science is progressive. We quote again from his *Thoughts and Conclusions*. (The reader will remember that he refers to himself in the third person.) "In the mechanical arts and their history, especially when compared with philosophy, he observed the following happy omens. The mechanical arts grow towards perfection every day, as if endowed with the spirit of life. Philosophy is like a statue. It draws crowds of admirers, but it cannot move. With their first authors the mechanical arts are crude, clumsy, and cumbersome, but they go on to acquire new strength and capacities. Philosophy is most vigorous with its earliest author and exhibits a subsequent decline. The best explanation of these opposite fortunes is that in the mechanical arts the talents of many individuals combine to produce a single result, but in philosophy one individual talent destroys many. The many surrender themselves to the leadership of one, devote themselves to the slavish office of forming a body-guard in his honour and become incapable of adding anything new. For when philosophy is severed from its roots in experience, whence it first sprouted and grew, it becomes a dead thing."

Such were the reasons why Bacon devoted himself to undermining the reputation of the leaders of the various philosophic sects, particularly the Aristotelians and the Platonists. He refused to follow them into the minute details of their writings and quarrel with individual conclusions to which they had come. For his criticism was not that they did not know their own business; on the contrary he thought that they were past masters at it. His quarrel was with the business itself. For reasons which we shall later consider more fully he regarded the disputatious philosophy of the Greeks as intellectually brilliant but morally corrupt.

Bacon thus, in complete isolation, was fighting for something which it is a feeble comparison to say he valued more than life itself. What was at issue was not his own career but the fate of mankind. He was fighting for the idea that the application of man's organized efforts to secure increased mastery over nature was a loftier purpose than that served by the philosophical schools of antiquity or the monastic life of the Middle Ages. He detested self-revelations, but whenever he painted the portrait of his ideal philosopher pity for mankind is the dominant moral trait. In the *Refutation of Philosophies*, when the philosopher comes in before his audience of sages to deliver his oration, we are told that: "He looked very quiet and serene, save that his countenance was habituated to the expression of pity." In the *New Atlantis* the Father of Solomon's House is similarly described: "He was a man of middle stature and age, comely of person, and had an aspect as if he pitied men."

We must now leave these absorbing writings, so little heeded and so little read, in which we see a new human conscience struggling to be born, and turn to consider the external circumstances of the man who wrote them.

Perhaps it is unfair to include his marriage among his external circumstances, but it is not easy to discover any romance in Bacon's life. Early in 1607 he married Alice Barnham, an alderman's daughter, of whom he said that she was "an handsome maiden" and "to my liking." A private letter of the time adds the facetious touch which no marriage is allowed to escape: "Sir Francis Bacon was married yesterday to his young wench in Maribone Chapel. He was clad from top to toe in purple, and hath made himself and his wife such a store of fine raiments of cloth of silver and gold that it draws deep into her portion." Not a word more is heard about the marriage for twenty years, which argues a considerable degree of success. But Bacon then struck her out of his will for some grave fault unspecified. The circumstances of her remarriage after his death suggest that her affections had already been transferred.

About the same time as his marriage the solicitor-generalship, which had been denied him by Elizabeth twelve years before, was given him by James. His ambition for a public career, reluctantly abandoned, again revived. The clash between his public and private ambitions must have been at this time at its height. His strength was no longer so great as it had been, and he was deeply engaged with the maturing of his philosophical designs. It is indeed at this date that we first begin to hear of a comprehensive title for his projected philosophy. It was to be called *The Great Instauration* and was to be in six parts. The composition of one part, the *Novum Organum*, for which the *Cogitata et Visa* was a sort of draft, was begun. But this was not a composition that could be hurried. With it Bacon intended to reveal the full scope and novelty of his design. Meanwhile some other publication was desirable, which, like *The Advancement of Learning*, would enhance his reputation and prepare the way for the full project, without too great shock to opinion.

This, his third publication, which came out towards the end of 1609, was the *De Sapientia Veterum* (On the Wisdom of the Ancients). Its being written in Latin is proof that he had the international republic of the learned

71

in view. He was at the same time negotiating to have the *Advancement* translated into the same language. One of his anxious concerns at this time was to find collaborators in Europe. Simultaneously he was circulating his other writings, the *Thoughts and Conclusions* and the *Refutation of Philosophies*, privately to selected individuals. And, while the prospects of a public career were now, somewhat late in life, brightening (or darkening) about his steps, his wonder whether he should not leave all this public business forever behind him is vividly revealed in a plan to secure what he called "command of wits and pens." By this he meant that he would have welcomed appointment to the headship of some college. He thinks of Westminster, Eton, Winchester; Trinity College or St. John's in Cambridge; or Magdalen in Oxford.

Once there he would have known what to do. He had various plans in mind. He wanted to encourage the study of natural philosophy. He thought in particular of the foundation of a college for inventors with all the necessary equipment. He planned the introduction of some system of rewards for the successful and dismissal for the incompetent. He saw the need for two large inquiries, one into curiosities of nature, the other into the history of the mechanical arts. He hoped to be able to endow four young scholars to do the necessary research. Grants would also be needed for traveling. Exchange of information would have to be organized with universities abroad. Such were the thoughts that ran in his head when his public position did not compel him to prepare papers about the state of the King's finances or the progress of the Scotch plantation in Northern Ireland.

V

1 6 0 9 - 1 6 2 0

IN A dedication to Bishop Lancelot Andrewes, prefixed to an unfinished work in 1622, Bacon describes the difference between *The Great Instauration* and his previous writings. The *Advancement* he called "a preparative or key, for the opening of the *Instauration*," and explained that it was "a mixture of new conceits and old." But of the *Instauration* he said that "it gave the new unmixed," and added that it was the work he "most esteemed." He also said he had "just cause to doubt that it flies too high over men's heads."

Before we consider the significance of the distinction Bacon draws between his two kinds of book let us pause to note the friendship between these two men. Lancelot Andrewes (1555-1626) was the most saintly of the Fathers of the Anglican Church, the most saintly and perhaps also the most learned. He knew Hebrew, Chaldee, Syriac, Greek, Latin, and ten other tongues. He was the leading figure in the commission of learned men which, between 1604 and 1611, produced the Authorized Version of the Bible. There is a parallel between this effort to provide England with a satisfactory version of the Scriptures and Bacon's project to interpret God's other book, the book of nature. In Bacon's own mind there was no conflict between religion and science. The absence of this conflict is shown by his conviction that he had Bishop Andrewes with him in his plan to find the key to the book of nature and also by the number of eminent clergy who were later associated with the early work of the Royal Society.

The intimate connection between his religious beliefs and his scientific ambitions explains many features of Bacon's work. We have seen in the first few pages of this book that he regarded himself as engaged in the effort to recover for man his lost dominion over nature. He thought this dominion had been forfeited by a false philosophy. It is for this reason that in Chapter IV we find him protesting that he needs to do penance for even discussing the opinions of some of the older philosophers, whom he calls unclean. He feels that they are not merely mistaken but sinful. They are unaware that science, like religion, must be known by its fruits. For this reason they fail both in humility before God and in loving service to mankind.

Remembering this religious aspect of Bacon's thought we may hope to find in the religious outlook of his day some light on the background of his thoughts. Not only was he, for instance, a Creationist, but he probably believed that the Creation had taken place at no very distant date. We put the origin of our world at some unimaginably remote date in the past and fill the gap between then and now by theories of development and evolution resting on a number of sciences of which Bacon had never dreamed. But in Bacon's day the total life of our universe in the eyes of believing Christians was not very long. Estimates, based on the genealogies in the Bible, might vary by a couple of thousand years, but nobody put the Creation quite so far back as 7000 B.C. In Bacon's day the most learned chronologer was Archbishop James Ussher (1581-1656). According to him the date of the Creation was 4004 B.C., and his system of dates was entered in the margins of the Authorized Version of the Bible in 1611.

There is no evidence that Bacon accepted these dates. He was probably as skeptical of them as was his contemporary Sir Walter Raleigh, who pointed out in his *History of the World* that the mature civilization of Egypt in the time of Abraham was incompatible with the orthodox chronology. But it is obvious that the universe did not present itself to Bacon in the same guise as it does to us. He apparently believed that not so many thousand years ago man had had dominion over it. He does not say anywhere that this means that man once had complete knowledge of how nature works, but the half-formulated thought is in his mind. Accordingly he calls the science he aims at an *instauratio*—that is, a restoration or renewal. He has confidence that man can acquire this knowledge because he once had it. In his optimistic moods he even fancies it might be done in a few years. It is an habitual

thought with him that speculative philosophy is so volu-
minous because it is an infinite repetition of the same
airy fancies, but that the book of nature when completed
would be much less bulky. He once suggests that a book
about six times as big as Pliny's *Natural History* would
suffice to contain all the facts necessary for a complete
understanding of nature.

Often his intuition of the reality of things breaks
through these narrow bounds. Instead of seeing science
as a return to a golden age he understands it as something quite new in the world. Instead of its being completed in a few years he thinks of it as growing generation
after generation. But the older way of thinking also has
its place in his mind. It explains his optimistic confidence
in the practicability of his plan. Naturally also it is particularly evident in his more popular works when he is
afraid of "flying too high over men's heads" and is offer-
ing them something more acceptable in the shape of "a
mixture of new conceits and old."

Such a mixture is the brilliant and attractive *Wisdom
of the Ancients.* Like the *Advancement* it is "a preparative or key for the opening of the *Instauration.*" But, while
it looks to the future, it also seeks to interpret the past,
for its underlying idea is the semiserious belief in the
existence of the true Baconian science in some remote
antiquity. This imaginary past he supposes to be reflected
in the early fables of the Greeks. Ranging, as his habit
was, over the literary tradition, or memory of mankind,
in his characteristic endeavor to relate man's thought to
his power over nature, Bacon paused at the mythological
period and asked what its significance was. "The most

ancient times," he writes, "except what is preserved of them in the Scriptures, are buried in oblivion and silence: to that silence succeeded the fables of the poets: to those fables the written records which have come down to us. Thus between the hidden depths of antiquity and the days of tradition and evidence that followed there is drawn a veil, as it were, of fables, which come in and occupy the middle region that separates what has perished from what survives."

That by a judicious interpretation one might pierce through the veil of fables to discover the lost wisdom of the earliest times had been a common belief. This right Bacon claims for himself. In one of the most graceful of all his writings he takes thirty-one fables and with exquisite ingenuity draws out of them his own political and scientific views. It is a book, as was said by one of his earliest editors, Dr. Thomas Tenison (1636-1715) "in which the sages of former times are rendered more wise than it may be they were by so dexterous an interpreter of their fables."

The writing was a favorite with Bacon himself. It was also a favorite with the learned public of Europe for which it was designed. But by writing it in Latin Bacon achieved the opposite of what he intended. He thought that modern languages, his own included, were not destined to last and would one day "play the bankrupt with books." To secure it immortality he wrote it in Latin. Singular misjudgment! In Latin its circulation has dwindled with every generation till it is now unread. It was soon translated but no English version has become popular, although Spedding's, from which we shall quote, might be thought to have deserved it. The importance of the book for Bacon's philosophy was not seriously appraised before Fulton Anderson's book appeared (1948). Spedding had placed it among the literary pieces.

An evidence of Bacon's pleasure in the work is the charm of the writing and the freshness of the fancy. Argument seems transformed into poetry. Expressing his conviction that the fables of the Greek poets represent an older wisdom, he writes: "They must be regarded as neither being the inventions of the poets themselves nor belonging to their age, but as sacred relics and light airs breathing out of better times, that were caught from the traditions of more ancient nations and so received into the flutes and trumpets of the Greeks." In his interpretations what is to be admired is not any affectation of success in arriving at the true original meaning of the fables —as if any such thing could be—but the ingenuity with which he draws from them the lessons he wants.

Thus one fable is boldly entitled *Cupid or the Atom.* It is recalled that the Greeks said that Love was the most ancient of the gods, that he was therefore the most ancient of all things whatsoever except Chaos, and that he had no parent. The application then proceeds: "The fable relates to the cradle and infancy of nature, and pierces deep. This Love I understand to be the appetite or instinct of primal matter; or to speak more plainly, *the natural motion of the atom;* which is indeed the original and unique force that constitutes and fashions all things out of matter. Now this is entirely without parent; that is, without cause. For the cause is as it were the parent of the effect; and of this virtue there can be no cause in nature (God always excepted); there being nothing before it, therefore no efficient; nor anything more original in nature, therefore neither kind nor form."

These speculations indeed pierce deep. Bacon goes on to acknowledge his debt to Democritus for this conception of an atom whose mode of existence is motion; and he expresses his sense of the superiority of this view of matter to that of the other schools. Their separation of matter from motion he calls a procedure "altogether blind and babbling." Bacon's conception of matter as essentially alive, a thing developing out of an inherent principle of motion, is one of the most important of his contributions to philosophy and points forward to modern evolutionary views.

It has often been made a reproach to Bacon that he naïvely and optimistically assumed that mechanical progress is in itself good. His critics cannot have read the interpretation of the fable which he calls *Daedalus or the Mechanic*. There, after speaking of the contribution of the mechanical arts to the culture of life in general, he adds: "Yet out of the same fountain come instruments of lust, and also instruments of death. For (not to speak of the arts of procurers) the most exquisite poisons, as well as guns, and such like engines of destruction, are the fruits of mechanical invention; and well we know how far in cruelty and destructiveness they exceed the Minotaur himself." Bacon knew as well as his critics that "the mechanical arts may be turned either way, and serve either for the cure or for the hurt."

In the fable called *Atalanta or Profit* he explains his view of the relation between pure and applied science, or what is now commonly termed long-term research and short-term research. Atalanta lost the race because she stopped to pick up the golden apple. She is the symbol for Bacon of that short-sighted mechanical ingenuity which is content with new inventions of limited scope but is incapable of comprehending the true goal, which is to grasp the hidden structure of the universe. But from that true picture of the universe, when it should be complete, Bacon expected, as we know, not only a contemplative satisfaction. It was also to be the means of endowing human life with new discoveries and powers, For then inventions would no longer come singly, but, as he himself says in *Valerius Terminus,* "in knots and clusters."

Diomedes was the Homeric hero who at the instigation of Minerva wounded Venus in battle. For a long time he escaped with impunity, but in the end it cost him his life. From this fable Bacon draws a warning against religious wars. The cause for which they are undertaken may be as pure and wise as Minerva; the enemy may be as corrupt and infamous as Venus; but they are little likely to achieve any enduring success. The true procedure in religion is to convince by force of reason and doctrine and by sanctity of life and by weight of examples and authorities. There were still burnings at the stake for religion in the England of Bacon. His own sect had produced such martyrs as Ridley, Latimer, and Cranmer. The beautiful conclusion of this fable has reference to them and all like them, to whatever sect they might belong. When Diomedes perished through the avenging power of Venus, his comrades, lamenting him, "were changed into a kind of swans—a bird which at the approach of its own death also utters a sweet and plaintive sound." Bacon makes use of this detail to enforce his lesson of the wrongness of religious persecution. "The sorrows and lamentations of the comrades of Diomedes, that is of those who are of the same sect and opinion, are commonly very piercing and musical, like the notes of swans, or birds of Diomedes. And this part of the allegory has a further meaning which is very striking and noble; namely that in the case of persons who suffer from religion, the words which they speak at their death, like the song of the dying swan, have a wonderful effect and impression on men's minds, and dwell long after in their memory and feelings."

But, of all the interpretations, that called *Prometheus or the State of Man* comes closest to the spirit and content of the full Baconian philosophy for which it was designed to prepare the way. The parable is too rich and too intricate to be easily summarized. Suffice it to say that it preaches eloquently the divine necessity for discontent. If the reader will remember that the name Prometheus stands for the present state of mankind, he will take the sense of our one short quotation readily enough. "Therefore let all men know that the preferring of complaints against nature and the arts is a thing well pleasing to the gods, and draws down new alms and bounties from the divine goodness; and that the levelling of accusations against Prometheus, yea, sharp and vehement accusations, is a thing more sober and profitable than this overflow of congratulation and thanksgiving. Let men know that imagined plenty is one of the principal causes of want."

Bacon, it is evident, had the conviction that a new mentality must be made to prevail among men if they were to have the courage and enterprise to go forward to the next stage. He knew that they would never improve either their science or the material conditions of their lives unless they could be lifted out of their habitual resignation. It is in the conviction that he was the chosen vessel for the new dispensation that he speaks out in the rousing prophetic tones of the fable of *Prometheus*. Here he shows us for a moment the mantle of the prophet, but it was to be eleven years yet before he donned it. All that time he let slip through his fingers before *The Great Instauration* was ready for the press.

The eleven years' silence between the two books was broken only by the appearance of the second edition of the *Essays* in 1612. These had now increased from ten to thirty-eight. The long silence was due to the fact that Bacon had allowed himself to be caught up again in the trammels of the public career from which with one part of his mind he longed to escape. In 1613 he became Attorney-General, in 1616 Privy Councillor, in 1617 Lord Keeper, in 1618 Lord Chancellor, and then Baron Verulam. Of his conduct in these offices we cannot write. It would be to stray from the biography of the writer to the history of his country. But it is clear that the pressure of public business retarded the accomplishment of his private dream, and when consciousness of advancing years forbade him to defer any longer the publication of the grand design it contained only fragments of the work he had projected.

Besides the *Essays* there are only the legal writings to

console us for the emptiness of these vital years. In the edition of Spedding, Ellis, and Heath, nearly five hundred pages are devoted to these writings. Not much needs to be said of them, however, since if all that remained of Francis Bacon were his contribution to law he would not be of much interest to posterity. Nor, even if that were not true, could much be said by the present writer, who has forborne to study closely what he could not judge without more legal training than he possesses. But it is at least worthy of note that even in Bacon's state papers and legal arguments his personal characteristics are not obscured. He still makes for himself vast designs which he executes only partially or not at all. His scientific interests force themselves into view. And the most refractory material is ever and anon transformed into literature by the stamp of his individuality.

He proposes to Elizabeth that he should deduce from the mass of material the fundamental maxims of the law and proceeds some distance with a work of that title. In the *De Augmentis Scientiarum* he suggests a Digest of English Law on principles that seem sound, but neither he nor any other has put the proposal into effect. So much for the grandiose projects. The original, and what I venture in contrast to the usual legal dryness to call sappy, quality of the writing wherever he gets the least chance may be illustrated from the *Arguments of Law*, which he dedicates to "My loving friends and fellows of Gray's Inn." He hoped that these pleadings might be specimens of advocacy such as had come down from Greek and Roman antiquity and such as he observed that the French published in his own day, and he seems to have hoped that his example might encourage literature to take root in the arid desert of the law. "These arguments which I have set forth are upon subjects not vulgar, and therewithal in regard of the commixture that the course of my life hath made of law with other studies, they may have the more variety." And so indeed they had.

One argument, for example, is concerned with property rights. When A has leased land to B with timber on it and the timber by act of nature or of man be severed from the ground, does the severed timber belong to the lessor or to the lessee? This puzzle gives Bacon an opening for natural history at the outset and for a famous image at the close: "Sense teacheth there be of the soil and earth parts that are raised and eminent, as timber trees, rocks, houses. There be parts that are sunk and depressed, as mines which are called by some *arbores subterraneae* [underground trees],—because that as trees have great branches, and smaller boughs, and twigs, so they have in their region greater and smaller veins." The date of this is 1616, and it is amusing to observe how the parched heart of the Attorney-General is panting for Biringuccio. It was from him, or one of his copyists, that he took his image of the mine as a tree. As for the peroration of this argument, it is worthy of the *Essays:* "And for the timber of this realm, 'tis *vivus thesaurus regni* [the living treasure of the kingdom]; and 'tis the matter of our walls, walls not only of our houses, but of our island." Into the stuffy courtroom comes the vision of the sea, bearing on her bosom the wooden walls of England. When his public career had ended, what Bacon wrote to entertain his leisure was not a history of property but a *History of the Winds.*

At last, however, in 1620, *The Great Instauration* appeared, and it is then that the mantle of the prophet is for the first time confidently and publicly assumed. Before we examine the contents of this book—it is a sort of omnibus volume made up of ten items—let us first hear what his secretary Rawley has to say about it: "I have been inclined to think, that if there were a beam of knowledge derived from God upon any man in these modern times, it was upon him. For though he was a great reader of books, yet he had not his knowledge from books, but from some grounds and notions from within himself; which, notwithstanding, he vented with great caution and circumspection. His book *The Great Instauration,* which in his own account was the chiefest of his works, was no slight imagination or fancy of his brain, but a settled and concocted notion, the production of many years labour and travail. I myself have seen at the least twelve copies of the *Instauration,* revised year by year one after another, and every year altered and amended in the frame thereof, till at last it came to that model in which it was committed to the press."

The title page tells us that the book is *The Great Instauration* of Francis of Verulam, Lord Chancellor of England. This has a grander ring about it than the *Mr. Bacon in Praise of Learning* of former, humbler days. It was no doubt some compensation for the endless delays, and some guarantee of a larger and more attentive audience, that the message when delivered should be

delivered by one in so exalted a station. The illustration
shows us a contemporary three-master plowing the waves
under full canvas to pass between narrow pillars. The
pillars are commonly explained as the Pillars of Hercules,
but this is only part of their meaning. In the first words
of his Preface the author interprets them more fully. He
says that men place too high an estimate on the present
state of their fortunes and too low an estimate on their
power to improve it, and that these are the two fatal
pillars which doom them to remain confined within a
landlocked sea and never venture out into the ocean of
knowledge. On a scroll under the illustration is a Latin
quotation from the Book of Daniel (xii, 4), which means
"Many will pass through and knowledge will be increased." In the body of the work (*Novum Organum,* I,
93) it is explained that this scriptural prophecy plainly
implies that an increase in knowledge will coincide in
time with the opening up of the globe by transoceanic
navigation. Every detail of the illustration is carefully
chosen to carry as much as possible of the author's meaning. We have already commented on the legend in the
scroll at the bottom—*Moniti Meliora.*

Next comes a brief statement, some five or six hundred
words in all, written in the third-person style Bacon had
experimented with in his *Thoughts and Conclusions.* Here
the meaning of the Latin word *Instauratio* is made clear.
It is stated that the most important of all earthly concerns is that the commerce of the mind with things should
be *restored* to its original perfection or at least improved.
The impossibility of doing this by means of the old philosophies is stressed and the need is proclaimed of under-

taking a total reconstruction of the sciences, the arts, and all human knowledge.

After this comes the Epistle Dedicatory to King James. Bacon had in hand (as Dr. Tenison put it) "a work for a man of a thousand hands and as many eyes." He knew that it was not an undertaking for a subject but for a king. For he did not project only an improvement of logical method, which might be undertaken by one man. What he had in view "depended" (in Tenison's phrase) "upon a distinct and comprehensive history of nature." He wanted the King to sponsor and finance the compilation of an encyclopedia of nature and the arts. Without this he was convinced that his design had no hope of a successful issue, and he knew that a work of the scope he projected could only be compiled by hundreds of men in many countries of the world collaborating under direction for years, possibly for generations.

In the Epistle Dedicatory he writes: "After my death I may yet perhaps, through the kindling of this new light in the darkness of philosophy, be the means of making this age famous to posterity; and surely to the times of the wisest and most learned of kings belongs of right the regeneration and restoration of the sciences. Lastly, I have a request to make—a request no way unworthy of your Majesty, and which especially concerns the work in hand; namely, that you who resemble Solomon in so many things—in the gravity of your judgments, in the peacefulness of your reign, in the largeness of your heart, in the noble variety of the books you have composed—would further follow his example in providing for the collecting and composition of a Natural and Experimental History, true and severe, unincumbered with literature and book-learning, such as philosophy may be built upon,—such, in fact, as I shall in its proper place describe: that so at length, after the lapse of so many ages, philosophy and the sciences may no longer float in air, but rest on the solid foundation of experience of every kind, and the same well examined and weighed. I have provided the machine, but the stuff must be gathered from the facts of nature."

After the Dedication comes the Preface, an essay between three and four thousand words in length and of extraordinary power. As the Dedication was addressed to the King, so the Preface is addressed to the people. It instructs, warns, admonishes, appeals. To those who believe in the old logic he remarks that "Logic is not nearly subtle enough to deal with nature." To encourage others he speaks of his own weakness. He says that it is "only by relying on the divine assistance that he has been able to uphold his mind against the shocks of hostile opinion and against his own private and inward hesitations and scruples, not to speak of the fogs and clouds of nature." He pleads above all else for the work to be undertaken in the spirit of charity. "Lastly, I would address one general admonition to all, that they consider what are the true ends of knowledge, and that they seek it not either for pleasure of the mind, or for contention, or for superiority to others, or for profit, or fame, or power, or for any of these inferior things; but for the benefit and use of life; and that they perfect and govern it in charity. For it was from lust of power that the angels fell, from lust of knowledge that man fell; but of charity there can be no excess, neither did angel or man ever come in danger by it."

One more quotation from the Preface: "The requests I have to make are these. Of myself I say nothing; but in behalf of the business which is in hand I entreat men to believe that it is not an opinion to be held, but a work to be done; and to be well assured that I am labouring to lay the foundation, not of any sect or doctrine, but of human utility and power." *It is not an opinion to be held, but a work to be done.* In other words, Bacon hopes to see research institutes set up and the arts and crafts renovated in the manner so vividly described later in his fiction of *The New Atlantis.* He meant not simply to write a book. *The Great Instauration* was not dictated by literary ambition. It was a blueprint for a new world.

The wonderful Preface completed, Bacon next proceeds to what he calls The Plan of the Work—that is, the description of the six parts designed to be included in *The Great Instauration,* should it ever be finished. The six projected parts are the following:

1. The Divisions of the Sciences.
2. The New Organon, or Directions concerning the Interpretation of Nature.
3. The Phenomena of the Universe, or a Natural and Experimental History for the Foundation of Philosophy.
4. The Ladder of the Intellect.
5. The Forerunners, or Anticipations of the New Philosophy.
6. The New Philosophy, or Active Science.

Of these six parts Bacon tells us that the first is wanting, but that the Second Book of his *Advancement of Learning* may be accepted as filling the gap for the time being.

The second of the six parts is the *Novum Organum,* the two books of which form the bulk of the volume called *The Great Instauration.*

The third of the six parts of *The Great Instauration* was to be the *Encyclopedia of Nature and of Art,* and of this he includes in the same volume a brief description with some rules to guide its composition. This is called the *Parasceve,* a word borrowed from the Latin New Testament, which means the day of preparation for the Sabbath. Bacon implied that when this great *Encyclopedia* should have been made, a new epoch, a sort of Sabbath, would have begun for mankind.

Since this would take a considerable time, perhaps some generations, he proposed a fourth part of the *Instauration* which he called *The Ladder of the Intellect.* No part of this was printed, but its purpose was made clear. It was to show in certain limited but specially significant fields how the logic (part two of the *Instauration*) was to be applied to the interpretation of the facts assembled in the *Encyclopedia* (part three of the *Instauration*).

The fifth part, which he called *The Forerunners* or *Anticipations of the New Philosophy,* and of which also nothing was as yet published, was to offer certain foretastes of the new knowledge and power that would belong to man when the *Instauration* was complete. They might be described as windfalls picked up on the way to the new philosophy, neither to be despised nor yet mistaken for the ripe fruit which the mature philosophy would yield.

The sixth part of the *Instauration,* the *New Philosophy,* or *Active Science,* must be left to Bacon himself to describe. "The sixth part of my work for which the rest are but the preparation, will reveal the philosophy which is the product of that legitimate, chaste, and severe mode of enquiry which I have taught and prepared. But to perfect this last part is a thing both above my strength and beyond my expectation. What I have been able to do is to give it, as I hope, a not contemptible start. The destiny of the human race will supply the issue, and that issue will perhaps be such as men in the present state of their fortunes and of their understandings cannot easily grasp or measure. For what is at stake is not merely a mental satisfaction but the very reality of men's wellbeing, and all his power of action. Man is the helper and interpreter of Nature. He can only act and understand in so far as by working upon her or observing her he has come to perceive her order. Beyond this he has neither knowledge nor power. For there is no strength that can break the causal chain: Nature cannot be conquered but by obeying her. Accordingly these twin goals, human science and human power, come in the end to one. To be ignorant of causes is to be frustrated in action."

Such was the plan of *The Great Instauration.* Much of it was not yet written. In comparison with the whole project not very much more was ever to be written. We reserve for our next chapter the examination of the more essential parts of it.

VI

FOR three hundred years the *Novum Organum* or *New Logic* has excited much admiration and some misunderstanding. It is hoped that what is written here will do nothing to lessen the admiration and something to remove the misunderstanding. A book written for the youthful reader has an especially good chance to do the latter. A frequent saying of Bacon's was that, in order to get on the right path again, philosophy must obey the scriptural injunction and become as a little child. By that he meant that it must lay aside all its book-learning and make a fresh start. He wanted men to get again into direct contact with nature, to see things with fresh eyes, and to create a new store of knowledge. This he described as "a Natural and Experimental history, unencumbered with literature and book-learning."

In advancing this project Bacon was making a sharp

break with the whole tradition of learning. We can understand better what he was after if we ask what he meant by the word *experimental* in the phrase we have quoted above—"a Natural and Experimental history." The word *experimental* has with us acquired new associations and a more precise meaning than it had in Bacon's day. It is now most commonly used in the phrase *experimental method* and its association is with the trained investigator in the laboratory. In Bacon's day it had not yet fully acquired this meaning and these associations. He used it in a broader sense to cover every kind of purposive interference with nature. This included all the processes of industry, all the arts and crafts associated with agriculture and manufacture. From this point of view we can better understand Bacon's aim. By a Natural History he meant a description of nature when left to herself; by Experimental History he meant a description of all that man does to interfere with or control nature, whether as scientist or producer. The latter he described as the more original part of his plan.

It is, of course, the natural outcome of the idea which had gripped Bacon as a boy. He had then revolted from Aristotelianism because it was barren of works useful for the life of man. He did not consider the Aristotelian logic faulty in itself, but thought that it was designed for an end different from his own. Aristotelian logic had been studied in England for about four hundred years when Bacon wrote *The Great Instauration*. It had profoundly affected the mental life of the country. It was, as Bacon said, fruitful in arguments. But it had had no effect on production, which was the question with which Bacon was concerned. It could not produce new arts.

It is just here that we see the significance of the Experimental History. Aristotle, in his *History of Animals,* had written very good natural history. His logic was most helpful for the building up of the classificatory sciences for which it was designed. But Bacon wanted to restore to man dominion over nature, to enable him to control and alter and improve on nature, and here Aristotle did not help. It was Bacon's great intuition that in order to effect this purpose the description and classification of nature as she exists free and unconfined should be supplemented by the description and analysis of nature as she has been vexed, imprisoned, bullied, forced, violently interfered with, or in any way affected, by the activity of man. Again and again Bacon comes back to this point. The contrast between what he calls *natura libera* and *natura vexata* is fundamental in his thought.

Let us put this in another way. The raw material for the contemplative science of Aristotle could be gathered by the contemplation of nature. The raw material for the active philosophy of Bacon could be gathered only from the examination of man's action on nature. An industrial history in the broadest sense must be the basis for a fresh advance in industry. A scientific industry must be based on the study of man's earlier and less scientific efforts to subdue nature to his own ends. Aristotle's logic was an aid to thinking; its goal was logical consistency. Bacon's logic was a guide to action; its test was whether it worked.

In pursuance of these ends Bacon sought to bring about a revaluation of the esteem in which various branches of learning were held. In his private notes of the year 1608 he speaks of endeavoring "To abase the price of professory sciences," professory sciences being those which have no issue in action. In *The Great Instauration* he is more explicit. He there remarks: "The philosophical tradition is but a succession of masters and scholars, not of inventors and improvers of inventions."

So anxious was Bacon that his thought should be fully understood on a point involving so great a breach with the philosophical tradition that he returned to the topic in the *De Augmentis* (1623), three years after the publication of the *Instauration*. There (Book II, Chapter 2) he first urges again the necessity of including the History of the Arts as a species of Natural History. Then he makes a further point. He complains of "the premature despair in human enterprises" which has arisen from the error of supposing that art is "merely an assistance to nature, having only the power to finish what nature has begun, to correct her when lapsing into error, or to set her free when in bondage," and of failing to realize that art can "change, transmute, and fundamentally alter nature." The cure for this despair is the History of the Mechanical Arts, which is "the most radical and fundamental towards natural philosophy; such natural philosophy I mean as shall not vanish in the fumes of subtle or sublime speculations, but such as shall be operative to relieve the inconveniences of man's estate. For it will not only be of immediate benefit, . . . but will give a more true and real illumination concerning the investigation of the causes of things and axioms of art than has hitherto shone upon mankind."

This breach with the philosophical tradition involved a

changed attitude toward the great query which for two thousand years had stood at the entrance of European philosophy. Is it possible for us to know truth? We judge of the external world on the evidence of our senses. How can we be sure that this evidence is trustworthy? Metaphysicians still give different answers to this question. The differences between the various schools of philosophy depend on the answer they give. Life, on the other hand, cannot wait for this difficult matter to be settled. It ignores what are called the metaphysical foundations of knowledge and proceeds with its practical task of making the best of what it seems to know.

In this matter Bacon was on the side of the practical man, though he had not adopted this position without reflection. One of his best editors, Ellis, says: "Though he often speaks about the errors and shortcomings of the senses, Bacon had yet never been led to consider the question which stands at the entrance of metaphysical philosophy, namely whether the subjective character of sensation does not necessarily lead to scepticism, if no higher grounds of truth can be discovered." It is not clear what Ellis means by saying that Bacon had never been "led to consider" this question. It sounds like a polite way of saying that he was too ignorant to have realized its importance. But in fact deliberate choice was involved. Bacon thought that to *begin* from the question of the validity of our knowledge was a mistake. That was, perhaps, where we might *end*. Accordingly he commended the practice of the oldest Greek philosophers who flourished at a period before this problem of truth (the epistemological problem, as it is called) had come to dominate philosophy and spread skepticism. Of these older Greeks Bacon writes: "Though they often bitterly complained of the difficulty of research and the obscurity of nature, still, like eager horses champing at the bit, they none-the-less followed up their object and came to grips with nature, thinking, no doubt, that this very question, whether knowledge is possible or not, must be settled not by arguing but by trying." (Preface to *Novum Organum*.)

We shall be concerned in what follows with Bacon's contribution to logic and with the rules for scientific investigation which he drew up. The relation of the new Baconian logic to the old Aristotelian logic will require further elucidation. But for the moment the all-important thing to remember is the novelty of Bacon's aim. He was not proposing to teach men how to argue correctly, but how to invent new arts. He complains of "the unkind and ill-starred divorce between the empirical and the rational faculty, which had thrown into confusion all the affairs of the human family." He proposes to remarry them in the interest of human well-being. "Out of this marriage," he writes, "let us hope there may spring helps to man, and a line and race of inventions that may in some degree subdue and overcome the necessities and miseries of humanity."

The Great Instauration, then, was intended not only as a contribution to philosophical literature but also as the blue-print for a revolution in production. The *Novum Organum*, or *Directions concerning the Interpretation of Nature*, which forms the logical part of it, is not like any other book of logic ever published. If it is detached from its setting in the plan of *The Great Instauration* and

treated simply as a contribution to logic, it becomes difficult to understand. Editors have sometimes aggravated
this confusion. Fowler's edition of the *Novum Organum,*
for example, which is the most elaborate edition of any
work of Bacon's that has ever been made, errs in this respect. He lists ten ways in which Bacon influenced later
generations. Only in the eighth place does he mention
"the furtherance of man's estate and the increase of his
command over the comforts and conveniences of life."
Apart from putting near the end of the list what Bacon
put at the top, Fowler is also guilty of misrepresentation.
He speaks reproachfully of "the manner in which Bacon
insisted on the subordination of scientific enquiries to
practical aims." This is a serious error. Bacon insisted
again and again on the virtual identity of scientific truth
and practical utility. "What is most useful in practice is
most correct in theory." (*Novum Organum,* II, 4.) "The
improvement of man's mind and the improvement of his
lot are one and the same thing." (*Thoughts and Conclusions.*)

Bacon's logic, or all that he managed to write of it, is
in two books. The first, which will occupy us throughout
the rest of this chapter, is introductory. It is a sort of final
draft of the many unpublished writings which we have
examined in earlier chapters. In particular it repeats and
expands the substance of *Thoughts and Conclusions.* But,
whereas *Thoughts and Conclusions* is presented as a con-
tinuous argument, the *Novum Organum* is cast into the
form of a series of aphorisms. There are one hundred and
thirty in Book I and fifty-two in Book II. Some of them
are quite short, but they tend to grow longer and longer,

until the word aphorism hardly seems appropriate for what is really a chapter, which may contain as many as forty numbered paragraphs (e.g., Aphorism 13, Book II). However the aphoristic form at least facilitates reference, and we shall insert the number of the book and the aphorism throughout our exposition for the sake of readers who want to consult the original.

The first book opens with the most famous of all the aphorisms: "Man is the helper and the interpreter of Nature. He can only act and understand in so far as he has observed Nature's order practically or theoretically. Outside this he has no knowledge or power."

Historically this is quite modern. The relation between man and nature is thought of in a new way. The world appears no longer as a vale of tears in which man makes a brief pilgrimage as a stranger from another realm. Instead, man and nature act and react upon one another. Nature acts upon man, for man has no knowledge or power apart from his understanding of nature's order. He must learn from nature. The function of his most precious and distinctive possession, his mind, is the apprehension of nature's order. But at the same time nature needs man. He is her helper and interpreter. He can understand her and make her do better than she does without his aid. The essence of human history is the record of this action and interaction between man and nature.

There is no doubt that Bacon was acutely aware of the novelty of this outlook on the world and society. Not only, as we have seen, did he suffer from "inward hesitations and scruples." He says also (I, 34): "Even to find out how to present my case is no easy matter. Things new in themselves will be understood on the analogy of the old." *

Not for nothing did he withhold his project from publication till he was nearly sixty.

The aphoristic style of the *Novum Organum* makes the individual points clear and impressive but tends to obscure the connections and the larger groupings of the ideas. These, however, can be discerned with a little patience. The first theme (1-4) is Man, the Helper and Interpreter of Nature. Here also is stressed the identity of knowledge and power. These are now familiar ideas and we shall say no more about them.

Next (5-17) come reflections on the sterility of the existing sciences and of the existing logic. The fifteenth aphorism contains a sweeping criticism of current ideas over which we must pause for a little. "There is no soundness," says Bacon, "in our notions whether in logic or in physics. The logical notions, Substance, Quality, Action, Passion, Essence even, are not sound. Much less are the physical notions, Heavy, Light, Dense, Rare, Moist, Dry, Generation, Corruption, Attraction, Repulsion, Element, Matter, Form, and the like. All are fantastical and ill defined." To make clear all that Bacon means by this criticism it would be necessary to trace historically the development of these notions. Then it would appear that, so far from being fixed and clear, they are confused and changing. The various schools of philosophy give different accounts of the meaning of Substance and Quality and their relation to one another. For the Greek physicists the Elements were Earth, Air, Fire, and Water. In recent times Paracelsus (c. 1490-1541) had analyzed matter differently into three principles which he called Salt, Sulphur, and Mercury. Bacon was taking leave to doubt the validity of all these concepts. He wanted to lay again the very foundations of knowledge. His idea was that with increased knowledge of facts we should be prepared to revise even our most fundamental notions, and that we must test our notions not only by their logical consistency but by their usefulness in action.

The sketchy notions which were the stock in trade of the traditional philosophers he called (26) *Anticipations of Nature* because they were not based on adequate experience. For them he proposed to substitute *Interpretations of Nature* based on experiment and observation. The contrast between *Anticipations of Nature* and *Interpretations of Nature* forms an important section of this Book (18-37). It indicates clearly the difference between the Aristotelian and the Baconian logic. Aristotle had, indeed, constituted the two great divisions of the art and science of logic, Induction and Deduction. By the process of Induction we rise from the particulars of sense to general notions. Deduction teaches us how to draw correct conclusions from these general notions. Bacon had no quarrel with the rules of Deduction as laid down by Aristotle. It was the science of Induction he sought to reform. The difference between Aristotle's way and his way he defines as follows: "Both ways set out from the senses and particulars and come to rest in the highest generalities, but the difference between them is infinite. For the first just glances at experience and particulars in passing, the second studies them in an orderly and systematic way." (22.) From the first method arise only Anticipations of Nature which can never be the basis of a true and active science. Bacon is emphatic on this point. "If all the wits of all the ages could meet in one place, combine their labours, and hand on their results, yet no great progress could ever be made in science by means of Anticipations." (30.)

Bacon had, of course, to ask himself why the mind of man should be so prone to go astray and so content to rest in superficial notions. This question he answers in his famous doctrine of the Four Idols (38-68.) By Idols he meant false ideas, or rather classes of ideas, in the mind which act as obstacles to the attainment of truth. His analysis of these false ideas has generally been recognized as a most valuable aid to the seeker after truth.

The first class he called Idols of the Tribe. These, he says (41), "have their foundation in human nature itself. It is a false assertion that the sense of man is the measure of things. On the contrary, all perceptions both of the sense and of the mind are according to the measure of the individual and not according to the measure of the universe." Bacon thought that as science advanced men would gradually substitute for their own limited and partial view of things a true picture of the order of nature as revealed by experimental science. He relied much more on experiment than on instrumental aids to the senses as the path to truth "according to the measure of the universe."

The second class are the Idols of the Cave. (The name is an allusion to the allegory in the seventh book of Plato's *Republic*.) These are the mistaken ideas of men derived from their heredity and environment. Bacon observes that every individual has his own peculiar nature;

also that he is influenced by his education, his friends, the books he reads, and so on. "The spirit of man," he concludes, "different in every man, is full of variety and perturbation, and governed as it were by chance." He had a shrewd eye for the extent to which man is a creature of circumstance. Here he is the forerunner of Robert Owen.

Thirdly there are the Idols of the Market-place. By this is meant the tyranny of words. Words are the medium of exchange of ideas. They must be adapted to the capacity of the common understanding if they are to circulate freely. Hence the emptier a word is of meaning the more popular it is. In the world of science as distinct from the world of politics we must not make decisions by counting heads. Words ought to be packed full of the considered results of experience before they can be a safe currency for science.

"Lastly there are the Idols which have immigrated into men's minds from the various dogmas of the philosophers. These I call Idols of the Theatre, because in my judgment all the received systems of philosophy are but so many stage-plays. They are worlds of illusion created each by its own author out of his literary imagination." (44.)

The summing up of the doctrine of Idols is as follows: "So much concerning the several classes of Idols and their equipage. All must be renounced and put away with a fixed and solemn determination, and the understanding thoroughly freed and cleansed. The entry into the Kingdom of Man, founded on the sciences, is not very different from the entry into the Kingdom of Heaven, whereinto none may come except as a little child."

We said at the beginning of this chapter that Bacon

intended a breach with the old philosophical tradition. Nothing could be more eloquent of this fact than the section which now opens. Here he turns to deal with the character of the old philosophies, but he resolutely refuses to discuss them in detail. This arises from the nature of his quarrel with them. It is near the truth to say that he did not think them so much intellectually mistaken as morally wrong. What he objected to was their uselessness. In seeking to undermine their authority, therefore, he proceeds as one would do who wished to teach how to distinguish weeds from useful plants or vermin from domesticated animals. The false philosophies or false sciences are to be recognized by certain external traits which he calls *signs*. The *signs* he gives are six: the place of their birth, the time of their birth, their inability to bear fruit, their inability to develop, the testimony of the philosophers themselves to the uselessness of their theories for action, and the diversity of opinions leading to interminable disputes. There is even a seventh *sign* in their popularity. Nothing that was not shallow could be so widely received. (69-77.)

A rapid summary of this topic of the *signs* will reveal, among other things, Bacon's historical sense, which is quite remarkable for his age. Bacon first notes that all the sciences of his day had originated in Greece. He then proceeds: "Now the wisdom of the Greeks was professorial and much given to disputations, a kind of wisdom most adverse to the inquisition of truth." We have already learned what Bacon meant by "professorial"—the kind of science which was handed on by a succession of masters and scholars, not by inventors and improvers of inventions. He is referring, in short, to the divorce of Greek science from the arts of production. "Their doctrines," he adds, "were for the most part what the tyrant Dionysius called them in order to make game of Plato: 'The talk of idle old men to ignorant youths'." (71.)

Furthermore, at the period when the sciences took shape "there was but a narrow and meagre knowledge either of time or place. The Greeks had no history that went back a thousand years, but only fables and rumours of antiquity. Of the various regions of the world they knew but a small portion. A multitude of climates and zones wherein innumerable nations breathe and live were pronounced by them to be uninhabitable. In our times, on the other hand, many parts of the New World and the whole of the Old World are known and our stock of experience has increased to an infinite amount." (72.)

"Of all signs, however, there is none more certain or more noble than that taken from fruits. For fruits and works are as it were the sponsors and sureties for the truth of philosophies. Now, from all these systems of the Greeks and their ramifications through the particular sciences there can hardly after the lapse of so many centuries be adduced a single experiment which tends to relieve and benefit the condition of man, and which can with truth be referred to the speculations and theories of philosophy." (73.)

The last *sign* we shall mention is progress. What is founded on nature, Bacon argues, grows and increases. The philosophies, like plants torn up by the roots, have lost contact with nature and never grow. The mechanical arts, however, founded on nature and the light of experience, continually thrive and grow. (74.)

Passing over the other *signs* we come to the next great topic, namely the *causes* for the state of affairs revealed by the *signs* (78-91). Here too his power of historical analysis is strongly in evidence. He first comments upon the fact that some periods are favorable to the development of science, others not. Out of the twenty-five centuries of recorded history only about six were fertile in sciences. "Time like space has its deserts and wildernesses." But even in times favorable for the growth of science, even in times of great mental activity, the subject least attended to was nature. Again, even when nature was the subject of study, it rarely enjoyed the full attention of any man throughout his life. "It has been made a bridge or passage to something else." No serious progress can be expected till natural philosophy becomes, to put it in our current phraseology, a first-priority and whole-time job.

Then the goal of science has been wrongly set. "The true and lawful goal of science is the endowing of human life with new discoveries and powers." But in general men are so far from setting before themselves the aim of augmenting the number of arts and sciences that they merely select from already existing knowledge what will help them to make money or reputation, or what they can use in their lectures. But not only are men ignorant of the true *goal*, they have adopted a wrong *way*. Instead of proceeding by experiment to get to grips with nature, they prefer to spin theories about her out of their own heads.

This preference for speculation over experimental research is bound up with a prejudice as old as it is hurtful. Men think that the dignity of the mind is impaired by long and close intercourse with the minute particulars of nature. They think the reason can get along by itself with the minimum of sense-evidence. They say that the mind ought to keep itself above matter. This is ruinous to the progress of natural philosophy. Experimental research is necessarily laborious; the actual subjects to be investigated are often in themselves ignoble; the subject does not lend itself to fine writing; the trades which bring men into contact with nature—those of the smith, the potter, the dyer—are reckoned illiberal; the facts to be considered are infinite in number and in subtlety. No wonder the study of nature makes no progress, when experience is not only neglected or mishandled, but even rejected with disdain! (83.)

Another cause of the slow and uncertain progress of science is superstition and immoderate religious zeal. The Greeks persecuted those who first ascribed natural causes for thunder and lightning. The ancient Fathers of the Christian Church condemned those who asserted the existence of the antipodes. The Schoolmen went too far in incorporating the contentious and thorny philosophy of Aristotle into the body of religion. Simple-minded divines think the study of nature is forbidden by Holy Writ. Crafty divines think that if the laws of nature are not known it will be easier to ascribe everything directly to the intervention of God. "They offer to God the unclean sacrifice of a lie." It is not surprising that the growth of natural philosophy is checked when religion, which has more power in human affairs than anything else, has been made to oppose it. (89.)

Again, the academic tradition is against science. In the customs and institutions of schools, colleges, and similar bodies destined for the cultivation of learning, everything is found adverse to the progress of science. For the lectures and exercises there are so ordered that to think or speculate on anything out of the common can hardly occur to any man. Studies in these places are confined and, as it were, imprisoned in the writings of certain authors, from whom if any man dissent he is straightway arraigned as a turbulent person and an innovator. "But arts and sciences should be like mines, where the noise of new works and further advances is heard on every side." (90.)

Finally the progress of science is checked because discoveries are not rewarded. It does not rest with the same persons to cultivate sciences and to reward discoveries. Moreover, apart from the absence of prizes and substantial benefits, invention has not even the advantage of popular applause. It is nothing strange if a thing not held in honor does not prosper. (91.)

Having thus dealt with the *signs* and *causes* of the corruption of the sciences, Bacon next proceeds to enumerate *grounds for hope*. Here also he is original and profound. He first deals with the subject of natural history, which must be the foundation of an active philosophy. The ground for hope here discovered is that, though existing natural history is radically defective, the remedy is clear. A kingdom or state, says Bacon, which tried to base its policy, not on trustworthy reports from ambassadors and other agents, but on the gossip of the streets, would suffer shipwreck. Such has been the course of philosophy. It cannot do without natural history, but in fact nothing has been duly investigated, nothing verified, nothing counted, weighed, or measured. The reason is that natural history has never hitherto been regarded as the necessary foundation of a philosophy of works. As soon as one attempts to use it for this purpose its hopeless inadequacy is revealed. But the remedy is easy. It is to collect *a natural history which includes, as a major part, the history of the mechanical arts.* The secret workings of nature do not reveal themselves to one who simply contemplates the natural flow of events. It is when man interferes with nature, vexes nature, tries to make her do what he wants, not what she wants, that he begins to understand how she works and may hope to learn how to control her. (98.)

This is one of the most fruitful of all Bacon's observations. The whole of history shows that science is the result not simply of observing nature but of interfering with nature. There was, for instance, obviously no more than a beginning of botanical knowledge so long as men were food-gatherers. To be a successful good-gatherer it sufficed to distinguish the edible from the poisonous fruits and to have some knowledge of the seasons. But when the step to agriculture and horticulture was taken, when man took the seed-bearing grasses and the fruit-bearing trees into his charge, when he protected, propagated, and improved them, he advanced to a new stage of botanical knowledge. Similarly the mineralogy and chemistry of the man who smelts metals and makes pottery and glass is at an altogether higher level than that of the man who has only learned to select and polish flints and other stones. Science is not created by thinking only, but by thinking about what is revealed by acting.

Bacon wanted an encyclopedia of the arts and crafts as a basis for a true philosophy of nature. He did not, however, want to confine science to the evidence that could be gleaned from the existing crafts. He wanted to devise experiments which would throw light on fundamental theoretical problems, though he believed these would later have practical consequences. He wanted to introduce what he called "experiments of light" (*experimenta lucifera*) as well as "experiments of fruit" (*experimenta fructifera*). (99.)

It might be asked why antiquity had not compiled an encyclopedia of the arts and crafts. In this connection Bacon lights on a truth which has become of great significance in our own day. Professor Gordon Childe, in his *Man Makes Himself,* has pointed out that the art of writing in early times was not used to record the processes of production, but was of service only to the arts of government. Bacon with an insight remarkable for his age had seen how difficult it is for science to progress without the aid of writing. "Hitherto more has been done in the matter of invention by thinking than by writing, and experience has not yet learned her letters. Now no course of invention can be satisfactory unless it be carried on in writing. But when this is brought into use, and experience has been taught to read and write, better things may be hoped." (101.)

Bacon's demand for this "literate experience"—that is to say, writing in the service of the arts and crafts—

would secure that all their processes should be written down and made available for study. This point recurs elsewhere in his writings, not without a slight confusion in terminology. The phrase *experientia literata,* which in Aphorism 101 means writing in the service of the arts and crafts, or recorded experience, is used extensively elsewhere (Aphorisms 103 and 110; *De Augmentis Scientiarum,* V, 2) in the more developed sense of a method of consulting experience which is systematic but falls short of the true Baconian method by not attempting to ascend to axioms. It contents itself with "experiments of fruit" and does not rise to "experiments of light."

Experiments of light, however, we must have. Bacon's intuition that the future course of invention would consist not in refinements of existing inventions but in the introduction of entirely new principles has proved true. New principles result only from experiments of light. With the coming of the industrial era invention passed out of the hands of the craftsman and into the hands of the scientific inventor and came to depend on the introduction of new principles. For thousands of years progress in reaping, for example, consisted in small improvements in the design of the reaping-hook. All these improvements were within the capacity of the reaper. But it was not a peasant who designed the reaper-and-binder; that was the work of a scientific inventor. Similarly the steam-engine was not a variation of an existing method of harnessing power. It does not use animal, water, or wind power. Steam was a new development involving research into the problem of latent heat. The same principle is exemplified by the development of electrical power, which required even more remarkable advances of theory than steam. That Bacon should have recognized so soon the need for the application of science to production is one of his greatest titles to fame.

Aware of the epoch-making character of the change which he foresaw and recommended, and anxious to bring forward every ground for hope that he could think of, Bacon at this point drops his habitual reserve and mentions himself. "I think men may take some hope from my own example. I say this not in order to boast, but because it is useful. If any be inclined to despond let them look at me, who being of all men of my time most busied in affairs of state, and a man of not very robust health (whereby much time is lost), and altogether a pioneer in my course, following nobody and sharing my counsels with nobody, have nevertheless, by resolutely entering on the true road and submitting my mind to Things, made, I may venture to say, some little progress. Then let them reflect what may be expected from men abounding in leisure, and working in association with one another generation after generation. For the path of science is not, like that of philosophy, such that only one man can tread it at a time. Especially in the collecting of data for the encyclopedia the work can first be distributed and then combined. Men will begin to understand their own strength only when, instead of many of them doing the same things, one shall take charge of one thing and one of another." (113.) The recognition that team-work and division of labor can be applied to science is again brilliant and original.

Book I of the *Novum Organum* is now approaching its end. Many important topics are raised in the concluding aphorisms. We shall allow space here for only one more, reserving the last aphorism for consideration when we turn to Book II. Aphorism 127 suggests the extension of the Baconian method of induction to fields other than the natural sciences. "It may be asked whether I speak only of Natural Philosophy, or whether the other sciences, logic, ethics, politics, should be carried on by this method. I certainly mean what I have said to be understood of them all." This is a striking recommendation to which we cannot give adequate attention in this book, but it may safely be said that the modern development of the social sciences has proceeded on Baconian lines. It has proved very fruitful to check the impulse to lay down the law for other men as to how they ought to think and behave and to substitute for this the patient inquiry into the history of how men have in fact thought and behaved.

Much has had to be omitted in making this short description of the contents of *Novum Organum*, I. But one thing could not have been left out without leaving everything out. That is, that Bacon was not proposing simply a revolution in knowledge but a revolution in the conditions of life. He knew how to make his point. "The difference between civilized men and savages," he said, "is almost that between gods and men. And this difference comes not from soil, not from climate, not from race, but from the arts." It was a revolution in the arts of life that the *Novum Organum* was intended to promote.

VII

THE first book of the *Novum Organum* is only an introduction to the logic itself. Much of it is devoted to criticisms of previous systems, and this Bacon himself calls *Pars Destruens,* the *Destructive Part* of his work. The constructive part, the actual method, the precise rules for induction, had yet to be produced. In some shape or form it existed in Bacon's mind, but the second book, the last that he completed, gives us only a portion of the whole design. Bacon enumerates nine parts of his method and treats of only one. Nor were the other eight parts ever reduced to writing or even sketched in outline though Bacon lived another six years and wrote voluminously. The *New Logic,* like most of *The Great Instauration,* remains a fragment.

The fragmentary state of the Logic requires particular examination. Many hold that the new rules of induction

114

were regarded by Bacon as his chief contribution to the restoration of science. In this belief they concentrate attention upon them and tend to isolate them from the rest of his work. The *Novum Organum* has often been published separately and the illusion has resulted that Bacon published a book with this title. This is not so. The book Bacon published was *The Great Instauration,* in which the *Novum Organum* was designed to be but the second of six parts. This is not intended in any way to minimize the importance of the *Novum Organum* either in itself or in Bacon's estimate of it, but only to make clear that his attempted reform of logic did not stand by itself but was part of a more comprehensive plan for the reform of life. This must be insisted upon. Otherwise his abandonment of the Logic at such an early stage of its progress is unintelligible. In fact, however, he himself tells us in the last aphorism of Book I that he proposed deliberately to leave it unfinished on account of its relative unimportance compared with another part of the plan.

There is another misunderstanding that must be cleared up before we can profitably discuss the details of the Logic, since it concerns the purpose for which the rules of investigation were designed. It is commonly alleged— and this is one of the most damaging criticisms leveled against Bacon as a reformer of scientific method—that he supposed himself to have invented in his Logic a method of discovery which could be mechanically applied to the interpretation of nature, which would make superior intelligence unnecessary and turn every industrious plodder into a revealer of new laws of nature. This supposed denial of the necessity of mental initiative and of exceptional mental powers is used to discredit his system. Before we examine what Bacon, in conformity with traditional practice, called his *logical machine*, let us inquire whether he really supposed it to possess this mechanical quality.

In the sixty-first aphorism of Book I Bacon uses language which has given rise to this misconception. He there says: "The course I propose for the discovery of sciences is such as leaves but little to the acuteness and strength of wits, but places all wits and understanding nearly on a level. For as in the drawing of a straight line or a perfect circle much depends on the steadiness and practice of the hand, if it be done by aim of hand only, but if with the aid of rule and compass, little or nothing; so is it exactly with my plan."

This, if taken out of its context, certainly does suggest that Bacon believed himself to have invented rules of induction which would level all intelligences and make every man capable of being a scientific discoverer. It is clear, however, from many passages in his writings that he did not mean this. We have already quoted in our third chapter (pp. 53-56) the autobiographical passage in which Bacon ventures to list the exceptional qualities of mind and spirit which he believed fitted him to be a pioneer in scientific discovery. This has passed into literature as a classical description of the scientific mind and temper.

To this it might be objected that Bacon thought his exceptional abilities were required to invent the method, which, once invented, would work almost by itself. This, of course, has an element of truth in it. But it still remains

116

clear that, even with the method, Bacon realized the necessity for superior ability in scientific research.

For proof of this let us turn to his *New Atlantis*. Here the scientific utopia, Bensalem, is controlled by an academy of scientists no more than thirty-six in number. They are men of superior understanding and character, and their special aptitudes are adapted to the different functions they supply in a complicated process of scientific research. Yet even among these academicians so far is invention from being mechanical that "upon every invention of value we erect a statue to the inventor and give him a liberal and honourable reward." So little did Bacon expect automatic progress that in his private notes (Spedding and Ellis, XI, p. 67) we find him occupied with the opposite problem, namely, how to get rid of scientists who within a reasonable time do not produce results. How then could he have believed that his method worked automatically? That the charge should be leveled against him is an indication that he is as yet imperfectly understood.

But, it will be said, the fact remains that Bacon did speak of his method as one that "leaves but little to the acuteness and strength of wits, and places all wits and understandings nearly on a level." We have still to inquire what he meant by this. The answer is not difficult. In this passage, as attention to the context makes clear, he is contrasting the condition of scientific progress with the very different condition which prevails in speculative philosophy. He looked upon the history of philosophy as consisting of a series of individual displays of brilliant intellectual powers which had achieved little or nothing

117

for the relief of man's estate or the true understanding of nature. For this he proposed to substitute a quite different activity, the taking of a vast inventory of natural phenomena by the organized teamwork of many men. He knew that to plan this inventory and to interpret it when made must be the work of superior intellect, of genius. He did not expect many men to be capable of this exalted task. But even these men would not need the literary gifts ° required to produce all the systems of speculative philosophy which Bacon dismissed as so many stage-plays. Furthermore, as the organization of research in Solomon's House in *The New Atlantis* makes clear, scientific work calls for various lower grades of intelligence also. Finally there were needed teams of collectors of information, who, if they would only stick to the plan, needed no exceptional intelligence to do useful work. Nothing, said Bacon, has been counted, nothing measured, nothing weighed. The counters, measurers, and weighers need not be men of exceptional acuteness or strength of wit.

While it is not true, then, that Bacon thought mental initiative and superior intelligence unnecessary for the scientific discoverer, it is remarkable that he saw so clearly the contribution to knowledge that could be made by men of average ability once science had been set upon the right track. This followed, of course, from his conviction that no sound philosophy of nature could be raised except on a foundation of fact infinitely richer than had ever before been attempted, or even dreamed

° Incidentally, the word *ingenium* (wit) refers especially to literary ability.

of. Let us now turn to consider the rules he laid down to guide men in the collection and interpretation of facts.

On the title page of the second book of his Logic he reminds us that his aim is not only to understand nature but to give man dominion over it. We are prepared, then, to find him begin with characteristic emphasis on the twin aspects of his philosophy: knowledge and power. In his first aphorism he states his object thus: "On a given body to generate and superinduce a new nature or new natures, is the work and aim of human *power*. Of a given nature to discover the form, or true specific difference, or nature-engendering nature, or source of emanation (for these are the terms which come nearest to the description of the thing), is the work of human *knowledge*."

What did Bacon mean by "generating or superinducing a new nature on a given body"? He meant something quite practical. His various extant writings supply abundant information of the kind of undertakings he had in view. Among them we find, for instance, a project for making metal alloys for a great variety of purposes; a project for making clearer glass, colored glass, unbreakable glass, heat-resisting glass; a project for making peas, cherries, and strawberries come early, and another for preserving throughout the summer oranges, lemons, citrons, and pomegranates. All these are examples of superinducing a new nature on a given body.

To go a little more into detail, one of his projects is to try incorporating iron with flint or some other stone to make what we would call steel. He hopes to produce a metal that will be lighter than iron and more resistant to rust. He suggests that its probable uses will be "*First* for

119

the implements of the kitchen: as spits, ranges, cobirons, pots, etc., *then* for the wars, as ordnances, portcullises, grates, chains, etc." (Spedding and Ellis, III, 799-836). So much for human power.

What Bacon meant by "*forms,* or the true specific difference, or nature-engendering nature, or source of emanation" has not been found so easy to understand; nor, perhaps, is it reasonable to expect that it should. For Bacon did not propose to begin his scientific revolution, but to end it, by defining these ideas. Still it is not difficult to get a rough idea of what was in his mind. Bacon found in Aristotle a fourfold doctrine of cause. Aristotle spoke of the material cause, the efficient cause, the formal cause, and the final cause as the four preconditions necessary for the existence or understanding of anything. For instance, in a statue the material cause would be marble; the efficient cause would be the sculptor; the formal cause would be the shape which he made the marble take; and the final cause would be the reason for which he made the statue. Bacon rejected the use of final causes in natural philosophy. He did not think it helpful to ask for what purpose things are as they are. But he retained the other three causes, giving them, as one would expect, a characteristic twist.

Bacon's aim, as we have seen, was to superinduce new natures on a given body. To do this it was necessary to have a knowledge of causes. But it is possible, he said, to possess this knowledge and power at two levels. If, for instance, you know how to make glass unbreakable or iron rustless, then you would know both the material and the efficient causes in these two instances. The material causes would be glass and iron, and the efficient causes would be the technical procedure which rendered them respectively unbreakable and rustless. That would be knowledge at the lower level. "A man who knows efficient and material causes," says Bacon, "can combine or separate or rearrange or improve things already discovered. He can even make new discoveries in a similar and prepared material. He cannot shift the deep-set boundary-marks of things." (S. and E., III, 793.) This lower level of knowledge is the domain of *experientia literata* in the second sense defined on pp. 110-11.

But Bacon was not satisfied with that. As we know, his ambition reached out after a more revolutionary extension of human power and knowledge. He was not concerned so much to improve existing inventions as to make radically new discoveries. A more penetrating insight into nature would, he thought, enable men to do this. It ought to be possible, for instance, not only to make *glass* unbreakable but to make *anything* unbreakable. It ought to be possible not only to make *iron* rustless but to exempt *every material* from the tendency to decay on exposure. This would be to know not only the material and efficient causes but the formal cause as well. The form of Permanence in its essential nature would be known. To quote again: "A man who knows forms can discover and produce effects which have never been produced before, effects which neither the changes and chances of nature nor the experience of human industry have ever brought to pass, effects which would never otherwise have suggested themselves to human thought." (S. and E., III, 794.)

In all this there was both a most penetrating anticipation of what the future of mankind was to bring forth and also a large share of illusion. Bacon thought it not impossible that, if science were vigorously prosecuted on the lines he proposed, men would quickly come to such a deep understanding of nature's secrets that their power over her would be practically unlimited. He held that the ultimate secrets of nature would prove to be very few in comparison with the vast variety of phenomena. He illustrated this by an analogy with language and the alphabet. The words in a language present such a bewildering variety of sounds that it is very difficult to analyze them. But, once the analysis has been achieved, the constituent elements of sounds (the vowels and the consonants) are very few. So is it with the phenomena of nature. The infinite appearances of things are nature's words. If we could press behind them to the hidden principles, the forms, which produce them all, we should find them to be few and simple like the letters of the alphabet. Once in possession of them we should be able not only to spell out nature's words more easily but even to make new words for ourselves.

Pursuing his theme of superinducing a new nature on a given body, Bacon at once introduces two new and suggestive ideas. He speaks of the *latent process* in every instance of generation or motion, and of the *latent configuration* in every body at rest. (Aphorisms 6 and 7.) By these terms he emphasizes that the real processes of nature are carried on at a level below the direct perception of the senses. In his opinion the great dividing lines drawn in nature up to his day corresponded only to the superficial appearance of things. Not even the new instrumental aids would enable the senses to cope with the subtlety of nature. Only carefully devised experiments, by means of which the experimenter actively intervened in nature's hidden processes, would enable him to proceed to a more correct anatomy. He adds that the deeper we penetrate in our understanding of nature the more powerful will be the forces we learn to control. These lessons were not lost. The influence of Bacon is often shown by the adoption of his vocabulary. An example is the name Latent Heat given by the chemist Joseph Black (1728-99) to his discovery of this phenomenon.

Bacon himself conducted an inquiry into the nature of heat, and his procedure and results are recorded in this book (Aphorisms 11 to 20). Consideration of them will help us to understand some of the peculiar features of his inductive process. In order to understand them we must remember that modern science did not yet exist and that Bacon was starting where the Greeks had left off. His complaint was that the fundamental notions current in natural philosophy had been derived by the ancients from a superficial acquaintance with facts. He called their method of induction Simple Enumeration. We can illustrate this by what the Greeks said about heat and cold. They analyzed existing things into four elements: Earth, Water, Air, and Fire. Two of these, they said, were naturally hot, namely Air and Fire; two were cold, Earth and Water; and everything was forced into this superficial classification. This old doctrine of the elements survived in the current Aristotelianism, and it must be admitted that it told one disappointingly little about heat or anything else. Nevertheless vague generalizations about heat and similar notions formed the basis of airy speculation not only in ancient philosophies but in modern ones constructed in the old way. Bacon's problem was how to break through to something more fundamental. He insisted that the new induction must cover a much greater range of facts and that it must sift the information obtained by a new method which he called that of Exclusions.

Beginning his investigations, Bacon first throws together almost at random a large collection of instances which agree in the presence of heat. He collects twenty-seven in all, ranging from the heat of the sun and of flame to such examples as the heat of friction and the heat of animal bodies. This he called a *Table of Essence and Presence* and trusted that the number and variety of his observations might prove helpful. This was already a great advance, for though it is only Simple Enumeration the range is extensive. By *essence* and *presence* he means that both the hidden cause of heat and the perceptible phenomenon of heat are present in each instance.

He next proceeded to sift his instances. Here the master idea was to isolate the subject of investigation by finding instances like the ones in which heat had been present, but distinguished from them by the absence of heat. This is not a very precise idea, but it can provide a clue to procedure, as examples will make clear. Sunlight was offered as the first example of heat. Moonlight is like sunlight in coming from a celestial source, but it seems to be without heat. This may be important. Bacon calls it a *negative instance* and continues his search for such negative instances. He could find no certain example of flame that lacked heat, but mentions the *ignis fatuus* and St. Elmo's Fire (phosphorescence in the sea) and suggests that more investigation of them be made. He fails also to find any example of a substance that is not heated by friction or of an animal that is not warm. In all he goes through a lengthy process, a new examination of natural phenomena, suggested by the twenty-seven positive instances in which heat was found to be present, and directed to finding similar conditions in which heat is absent. The results are finally set forth in the *Table of Deviation,* or *Absence in Proximity.*

He next proceeded to make a table of *variations* in the degree of heat either in the same body at different times or in one body in comparison with another. This procedure, the underlying idea of which seems still less precise than the former, leads to a result called the *Table of Degrees* or the *Table of Comparisons.* Armed with these Tables he proceeds to the work of Induction by the method of Exclusions. We can form a rough notion of how the method worked. By Exclusion he meant the rejection of a false theory. Thus, we might ask, is heat only a celestial phenomenon? No; fires on earth are hot. Is it then only an earthly phenomenon? No; the sun is hot. Are all celestial bodies hot? No; the moon is cold. Does heat depend on the presence in the hot body of some constituent part, like the ancient element of Fire? No; any body can be made hot by friction. Does heat depend on the texture of the body? No; a body of any texture can be heated. And so forth and so on.

This to us somewhat odd procedure has at least the

negative result of sweeping away survivals of the ancient Greek doctrine of the elements. But it did not seem likely to lead quickly to any decisive results. Bacon would reply that definite results could be expected only when progress had been made in a variety of different fields. But meanwhile he attempted a provisional solution of his problem by way of an hypothesis. This he had previously condemned as an *Anticipation of Nature,* but he now admits it as a temporary necessity. With his usual profusion of names he calls it an *Indulgence of the Intellect,* or a *Commencement of Interpretation,* or a *First Vintage.* In this task he acquits himself exceedingly well, coming to the remarkable conclusion that: *Heat is a motion of the smaller particles of bodies, in which a tendency to fly apart from one another is held in check.* This, of course, is a revolutionary advance on the old Greek doctrine.

In fact, where Bacon let his mind run ahead of the evidence he gave a fair example of the method of hypothesis which has been that of modern science. But it is certainly worthy of remark that the method of hypothesis, which has been found indispensable, is admitted by Bacon only as a *pis aller* and some explanation is necessary. The probability is that his yearning after the more perfect method of Exclusions rested on an illusion. He thought that the universe was a much smaller thing than it has proved to be. If he could really have collected all the important phenomena of the universe into a work about six times the size of Pliny's *Natural History* (as he once suggests), then it might have been possible to compile with great completeness the kind of Tables he recommends and to proceed methodically by the method of Exclusions. But this is a big *if*, and it indicates that Bacon, in spite of his keen vision of the future course of science, had also his blind spots.

Having given his Tables, illustrated his method of Exclusions, and reaped his First Vintage, Bacon gives a list of nine additional aids to the intellect which he intends to supply. "I propose to treat then in the first place of *Prerogative Instances;* secondly of the *Supports of Induction;* thirdly of the *Rectification of Induction;* fourthly, of *Varying the Investigation according to the nature of the subject;* fifthly, of *Prerogative Natures,* or what should be investigated first and what last; sixthly, of the *Limits of Investigation,* or a Synopsis of all Natures in the Universe; seventhly, of the *Application to Practice;* eighthly, of *Preparations for Investigation;* and lastly, of the *Ascending and Descending Scale of Axioms.*" (Aphorism 21.) Of these nine additional aids he handles only the first, to the discussion of which we shall come in a moment. The remaining eight were sacrificed to his decision to drop the Logic and devote himself to the next section of *The Great Instauration.*

What, then, should we think of this vast unfulfilled design? Two comments suggest themselves. First, I think we have clear evidence of the illusion under which he labored as to the size and complexity of the universe when he proposes to treat of the Limits of Investigation, and defines this as a Synopsis of all Natures in the Universe! It was prudent to stop before he got to this point. A more genuinely scientific reason for abandoning the whole scheme is suggested by the fourth item: *Varying the Investigation according to the Nature of the Subject.*

When he came to consider this, he must have seen that rules could not be laid down *in advance* and that only the man engaged on the research could determine how to vary the investigation. He saw that he was pursuing a will-o'-the-wisp in trying to trace out beforehand the path of advancing science in exact detail.

Although his abandonment of the Logic involves the admission that it was partly founded on an illusion, this by no means denies the value of the part he saw fit to execute. We must follow him now to his doctrine of Prerogative Instances, the main subject of Book II, occupying the remainder of the book.

The word prerogative needs an explanation. In ancient Rome the populace voted by tribes, and the tribe entitled to vote first was called *prærogativa*. Since the vote of the first tribe was generally decisive, the word acquired also this sense. By Prerogative Instances, then, Bacon means the kind of phenomena which should be sought out first as being likely to throw decisive light on any subject of inquiry. His general purpose in the whole handling of the subject is to suggest an appropriate strategy for the attack on nature. He seeks to direct attention to the weak places in her armor, to show how she can be surprised and taken off her guard. In all, he discusses twenty-seven groups of Instances which, under their fantastic names, conceal much that is helpful and to the point. If he does not often give the impression that he would himself be successful in the inquiries he suggests, he does inspire confidence that the interpretation of nature is not the hopeless enterprise previous philosophies made it appear. His influence on our vocabulary may here again be taken as proof of the effect of his doctrine on the development of modern science. We still speak of Solitary Instances, Glaring Instances, Crucial Instances, without any thought of the author who first gave these terms currency.

By *Solitary Instances* he means occurrences of a phenomenon freed from confusing association with other phenomena. The subject of our investigation is caught, as is were, alone. Suppose we are investigating the nature of color. Nature is full of colored things, but the combination of the colors with all the other qualities makes the investigation difficult. How convenient it would be if we could isolate color! Now the breaking up of a beam of light by a prism into all the colors of the rainbow affords an opportunity of investigating color by itself and observing how it is produced. It isolates the phenomenon. It is a Solitary Instance.

Crucial Instances are observations which enable us to decide between rival theories. An interesting point in the discussion devoted to them is the praise accorded to Gilbert—not, of course, for his cosmological speculations but for his observations on the magnetic needle.

Glaring Instances present the phenomenon under investigation in its highest intensity, and are of course of extreme importance for the researcher. But, says Bacon, he will be well advised to look also for the same quality in its feeblest and most hidden manifestations. These he calls *Clandestine Instances*. He hopes that the contrast between these two types of Instance may throw light on the genesis of the quality or form that is under investigation. Suppose we are interested in tensile strength. This is great in metals and other solids; but can it not be detected

129

even in liquids? Bacon has an interesting discussion of the cohesive force of liquids, what we now call surface tension. It is an attempt at discovering the Latent Configuration of the form tensility. I do not think it is useless. It fulfils his promise to go deeper into such superficial distinctions as that between liquid and solid. In a remote way it prepares the ground for such knowledge of molecular structure as explains the difference in tensile strength of graphite and of the diamond, both forms of carbon.

Under the title of *Conformable Instances* are discussed analogies between things natural and artificial, as between the eye and a mirror, or the shape of the ear and a place that gives a good echo. *Limiting Instances* are concerned with border-line cases, things between fish and animal, or animate and inanimate. We all know what importance these still have in science. Is the virus organic or inorganic? It has some properties of living matter, yet it can be crystallized. Bacon was right to direct attention to frontiers between species.

Under the strange title of *Instances of the Gate* are discussed instrumental aids to the senses—spectacles, the magnifying glass, the telescope. Here we find strong praise of Galileo. There is also the lively observation that if Democritus had got hold of a magnifying glass he would have jumped with joy at the prospect of seeing the atoms he called invisible. Another section, *Summoning Instances,* deals with the place of experiment in research. While instruments merely enhance the range of our senses, experiments—a more powerful aid to investigation—lay hold of the objects of our curiosity and summon them before the bar of our judgment.

Enough has been said to indicate the varied and stimulating contents of Book II. It remains to add that it must have been written before Book I took its final shape. Book I in its last aphorism announces the intention to leave the Logic unfinished. Book II ends with a confident promise of completion. "But now I must proceed to the supports and rectifications of induction, and then to concretes, and Latent Processes, and Latent Configurations, and the rest, as set forth in order in the Twenty-first Aphorism: that at length, like an honest and faithful guardian, I may hand over to men their fortunes, now that their understanding is emancipated and come as it were of age; whence there cannot but flow an improvement in man's estate, and an enlargement of his power over nature. For man by the Fall fell at the same time from the state of innocency and from his dominion over creation. Both of these losses, however, can even in this life be in some part repaired; the former by religion and faith, the latter by arts and sciences. For creation was not by the curse made altogether and forever a rebel, but in virtue of that covenant 'In the sweat of thy face shalt thou eat bread' it is now by various labours (not certainly by *disputations* or idle magical ceremonies, but by various *labours*) at length and in some measure subdued to the supplying of man with bread; that is, to the uses of human life."

VIII

THE 1620 volume, *The Great Instauration,* concludes with the two pieces named at the head of this chapter. The name *Parasceve,* which has now come to seem mysterious, is (as was said in an earlier chapter) simply the Vulgate word for the Jewish Day of Preparation for the Sabbath. It is Bacon's designation for the short writing in which he explains his purposed *Encyclopedia of Nature and of Art.* Presumably he chose it in order to suggest that when the work of the great instauration was done man would have accomplished his six days of creative labor and might settle down to the enjoyment of his Sabbath rest. It is naturally followed by the chapter headings of the proposed Encyclopedia.

It was in order to plan this Encyclopedia, give direc-

132

tions for its compilation, suggest the chapter headings, and try to get the work of investigation done, that Bacon gave up the effort to complete his Logic. We have just seen that the last aphorism of the Second Book of the Logic reveals his intention of completing the rules of induction. But the last aphorism of the First Book, which must have been written at a later date (presumably when he was preparing *The Great Instauration* for the press), announces the decision to abandon the Logic for the Encyclopedia and gives reasons for this choice. This aphorism, then, is the appropriate introduction to the *Parasceve*, for which reason we have reserved it for this place.

Every word of this aphorism is important for the understanding of Bacon's conception of his design. We shall therefore quote it in full. "The time has come for me to put before the reader my rules for the interpretation of nature. I think my rules are true and useful. But I do not say that they are either perfect or absolutely indispensable. I do not mean to suggest that nothing can be done without them. On the contrary I think that if men had available a good Encyclopedia of Nature and of Art and would work hard at it, remembering just two of my rules —first, to drop all preconceived notions and make a fresh start; and second, to refrain for a while from trying to rise to the most general conclusions or even near to them —they would succeed without any other rules of induction by the light of their own intelligence in falling into my method of interpretation. Interpretation is, after all, the natural work of the mind when it is not obstructed. I merely claim that my rules will make the process quicker and more reliable. I do not mean to say that they cannot be improved upon. This would be utterly at variance with my way of thinking. My habit is to consider the mind not only in its own faculties but in close connection with things. It follows that I must admit the possibility that the art of discovery itself will advance as discoveries advance."

We may remark in passing the modesty, candor, and common sense of this pronouncement; but what must particularly engage our attention is the information it gives that Bacon has now come to regard the Encyclopedia as more important for his purpose than the Logic.

His overwhelming sense of the importance of the Encyclopedia—which he suggested calling the Primary History or The Mother History, as the basis on which alone could be founded a true philosophy of nature—is expressed in the opening paragraphs of the *Parasceve* with a force unusual even in this most forceful writer. "What I have often said I must here emphatically repeat. If all the wits of all the ages had met or should hereafter meet together; if the whole human race had applied or should hereafter apply themselves to philosophy; if the whole earth had been or should become nothing but academies and colleges and schools of learned men; still without a natural and experimental history such as I am going to prescribe, no progress worthy of the human race could have been made or could be made in philosophy and the sciences. On the other hand, let such a history be once provided and well set forth, and let there be added to it such auxiliary and light-giving experiments as in the very course of the interpretation will present themselves or will have to be found out; and the investigation of nature and of all sciences will be the work of a few years. This therefore must be done or the business must be given up. For in this way, and in this way only, can the foundations of a true and active philosophy be established; and then will men wake as from a deep sleep, and at once perceive what a difference there is between the dogmas and figments of the wit and a true and active philosophy, and what it is in questions of nature to consult nature herself."

The *Parasceve* consists only of an introduction and ten aphorisms. So far we have quoted only from the introduction. As we advance into the aphorisms we find that Bacon is as concerned to stress the novelty of his plan as it importance. His first aphorism lays it down that nature exists in three states. Either she is free and unfolds herself in her own ordinary course; or she is forced out of her usual course by exceptional natural circumstances; or she is constrained and molded by man. "In things artificial nature takes orders from man. Without man such things would never have been made. By the agency of man a new aspect of things, a new universe, comes into view." This interpenetration of the human and the natural is the novel element in Bacon's thought. He proposes an inquiry into nature in her threefold character with a view to the conscious and planned development of this interpretation. This, he insists (Aphorism 2), is being undertaken for the first time. "For neither Aristotle, nor Theophrastus, nor Dioscorides, nor Caius Plinius, ever set this before them as the end of natural history."

Aphorism 3 insists on the difference between the new

workmanlike Encyclopedia he has in view and the semi-literary productions of antiquity. "Away with antiquities, citations, disputes, controversies, everything in short which is literary. For all that concerns ornaments of speech, similitudes, treasury of eloquence, and such like emptinesses, let it be utterly dismissed. No man who is collecting and storing up materials for ship-building or the like thinks of arranging them elegantly as in a shop, and displaying them so as to please the eye; all his care is that they be sound and good, and that they be arranged so as to take up as little room as possible in the warehouse. And this is exactly what should be done here."

Next we are cautioned that the information to be collected must be of wide range and adapted to the measure of the universe, not of man. "For the world is not to be narrowed down till it will go into the understanding, which has been the practice hitherto, but the understanding must be stretched and expanded to take in the image of the world as it is discovered." When this has been done we shall no longer be kept dancing within narrow circles like bewitched persons but shall range at large within the circuit of the whole world. (4.)

But to the attainment of this end it must be remembered that "the history of the arts is of most use. It exhibits things in motion and leads more directly to practice. It takes off the mask and veil from natural objects. As Proteus did not go through his changes till he was seized and handcuffed, so under the constraint of arts nature puts forth her ultimate efforts and strivings. Natural bodies refuse to be destroyed, to be annihilated; rather than this they will turn themselves into something else.

We must then set aside all delicacy and daintiness and concentrate specially on the history of the arts, mechanical and illiberal though it may seem. And here we must prefer the arts which expose, alter, and prepare natural bodies and materials; such as agriculture, cookery, chemistry, dyeing, the manufacture of glass, enamel, sugar, gunpowder, artificial fires, paper, and the like. The arts which consist principally in subtle motions of the hands or instruments are of less help; such as weaving, carpentry, architecture, manufacture of mills, clocks, and the like; although these too are by no means to be neglected, both because many things occur in them which relate to the alterations of natural bodies, and because they give accurate information concerning local motion, which is a thing of great importance in very many respects." (5.)

This recommendation to learn from the crafts was much heeded by the members of the Royal Society in its early days, and in the eighteenth century by Diderot and d'Alembert, the planners of the famous *Encyclopédie*. That it could also be carried to foolish extremes is shown by the case of Dr. Robert Hooke (1635-1703), a follower of Bacon, whose *General Scheme or Idea of the Present State of Natural Philosophy* was posthumously published in 1705. Coleridge, in *The Friend*, Section II, Essay 8, makes merry with his idea that the following preliminary studies will be requisite or desirable for the philosopher of nature: "The history of potters, tobacco-pipe-makers, glaziers, glass-grinders, looking-glass-makers, spectacle-makers, makers of counterfeit pearl and precious stones, bugle-makers, lamp-blowers, colour-makers, colour-grinders, glass-painters, enamellers, varnishers, colour-sellers, painters, limners, picture-drawers, makers of marbles, fustian-makers, tinsey-makers and taggers, school-masters, writing-masters, printers, book-binders, stage-players, dancing-masters, apothecaries, chirurgeons, seamsters, butchers, barbers, laundresses, etc. etc." But any good idea can easily be driven to excess.

Bacon himself in his *List of Particular Enquiries* (intended to form the sectional headings for the proposed Encyclopedia) avoids the error of losing himself in an indiscriminate study of an infinity of details. He gives one hundred and thirty different headings, one of which is: *Miscellaneous History of Common Experiments which have not grown into an Art*. Under this heading would have been included many of the small crafts and callings, the lessons of which are doubtless of some significance for the totality of human knowledge, but which are thrown into undue prominence by the indiscriminate zeal of Hooke and the comic genius of Coleridge.

In fact Bacon's plan for an encyclopedia is an event of historical importance. Like the rest of his philosophy, it is a sort of hinge on which we turn from antiquity into modern times. The nearest thing to it in antiquity was Pliny's *Natural History*. Its modern realization was, as we have said, the *Encyclopédie* of Diderot and d'Alembert. The first thing to admire in it is its main divisions. The first forty titles are devoted to external nature. Eighteen are then devoted to man himself; the remainder, seventy-two in all, to man's action on nature, his arts and crafts and sciences and so forth.

The main subdivisions in the first section are: Astronomy, Meteorology, Geography; next what he calls The Greater Masses, meaning Fire, Air, Water, and Earth, which are the four elements of antiquity but which are to be studied in the new Baconian way; and finally the various species of things, mineral, vegetable, and animal.

Man, the next of the great divisions, is to be studied anatomically and physiologically, in his structure and his powers, in his actions voluntary and involuntary, awake and asleep, in his conception and in his growth, in his life and in his death. We know from his other writings how convinced Bacon was of the possibility of curing disease, alleviating pain, prolonging life, and easing death.

The seventy-two sections devoted to man's activities considered in relation to his environment are not so easy to summarize. Here we are urged to study medicine, surgery, chemistry; the faculty of vision and the arts connected therewith—painting, sculpture, etc.; hearing and sound, and the art of music; smell and smells; taste and tastes; touch and the objects of touch, including physical love as a species of touch; pleasure and pain; the emotions and the intellectual faculties. After this we come to food and drink and the arts connected therewith; the care of the person; clothing, architecture, transport; printing, books, writing, agriculture, navigation, and other arts of peace; and the arts of war. The history of machines is included and, as a sort of afterthought, arithmetic and geometry.

Finally a note is appended about the difference in procedure between collecting the information and its subsequent handling. It is suggested that it may prove more convenient to collect the material with reference to the different Arts, but to arrange it with reference to the different Bodies. With this the *Parasceve* and *The Great Instauration* as a whole come to an end. The overburdened man of affairs had done what he could to pack within the covers of one book the hints and directions which he thought might suffice to teach his fellows to think with more intelligence and humanity about themselves and their world. *Homo naturae minister et interpres*—Man who obeys nature in order to understand and control her. The great idea had been furnished with such arguments as he could devise to explain and recommend it. Its issue would be not a book but the destiny of the human race.

IX

What Bacon achieved with the publication of
The Great Instauration - Bacon and the Bible - Bacon
and the Greeks - Bacon and Harvey

WITH Bacon we enter a new mental climate. When we
analyze it we find that it consists not so much in a scientific advance as in the well-founded confidence that the
life of man can be transformed by science. Bacon is not,
like other scientists, working in a chosen field in the light
of a long tradition. Rather he makes himself the herald
of a revolution in the life of humanity, which he calls a
birth of time.

This conviction of an approaching change in human
affairs is accompanied by a deepening historical sense.
The change is not something that is just going to happen,
but something that is to be brought about. Men must do
it or it will not be done. Bacon like so many others
imagined a utopia, but it is a utopia with a difference. It

is not just an ideal society existing perhaps in the past, but a society to be brought about by the new kind of knowledge. Bacon senses here a historical problem. What was the defect of the old knowledge that rendered it impotent? His great learning enabled him to consider historically the relation between human knowledge and human welfare. He refused to judge knowledge by a merely internal standard. It was not enough that it be logically consistent. He asked instead what it had done, how had it affected the fortunes of mankind down the ages. From this historical standpoint he proposed a new criterion of the validity of science. "Science, like religion, must be judged by its fruits."

This thought has many consequences. In the *Valerius Terminus* Bacon writes: "I find that even those that have sought knowledge for itself, and not for benefit or ostentation, or any practical enablements in the course of their life, have nevertheless propounded to themselves a wrong mark—namely, satisfaction (which men call Truth) and not operation." "Satisfaction, which men call Truth"—this is a shrewd phrase. Bacon means to throw doubt on the validity of knowledge which is held to be valid merely because it is logically self-consistent. He would still ask the question: Is it true? And this question he would seek to answer by operation, by putting the knowledge to the test of practice.

By his appeal to practice Bacon brushed aside the preliminary inquiry: Can man know truth? He looked upon this as a meaningless question and the breeding-ground of skepticism and inaction. He recommended men to stop debating the question and try. His attitude is not an evasion, it is a new and helpful approach. It offers a historical rather than a logical answer to the problem of truth. We must remember his formula of Man the Helper and Interpreter of Nature. Man cannot understand nature except in so far as he can coöperate with her. Knowledge springs not just from thinking but from thinking about what happens when we act. This is in line with our most recent conception of science which sees science as a record of *observations* rather than of *facts*. Observations always imply some interference by the observer, and the range of observation is always conditioned and limited by the theoretical and instrumental equipment of the observer. In this way the growth of science is connected by innumerable links with the general progress of society.

To illustrate this point, consider man's knowledge, say, of trees. We can say that there is a kind of knowledge of trees that is characteristic of the primitive food-gatherer and is adequate to his needs. There is another kind of knowledge of trees characteristic of the neolithic carpenter. He knows wood as well as trees. But the chemist and the botanist of today not only know wood—they know its composition and the way it grows. The food-gatherer's knowledge is a hundred thousand years old, the neolithic carpenter's about ten thousand years, the chemist's about one hundred. Here there is growth of knowledge, but the progress of this knowledge could not have been anticipated beforehand by a metaphysician debating the abstract question: Is the human mind capable of knowing the truth about trees? On the contrary, the growth of this knowledge appears to be inseparable from the general development of society. Bacon perceived this connection so far as it was visible in his day. Setting great store by the practical knowledge of early man, he yet wished to make the leap to scientific knowledge. When he spoke about *latent structure* and *latent process* he was groping after the kind of knowledge the chemist and the botanist now possess.

Growth in knowledge, Bacon insists, is only one aspect of a more general progress. "The improvement of man's mind and the improvement of his lot are one and the same thing." (*Thoughts and Conclusions.*) We must not understand by this that Bacon supposed that man needs nothing more for his happiness than increased control over nature. He knew very well and repeatedly insisted that material progress would bring men no happiness at all unless it were governed by the sovereign virtue of love. But he also insisted that love could achieve little without power. Looking into the historical process of the material and mental development of man he saw that inventions are the levers by which civilization is moved forward. A successful invention at once guarantees the truth and assures the utility of science. Let us, then, turn from the old knowledge which even makes a boast of its uselessness. Let us make a new inventory of man's achievement based on the criterion of its usefulness. On this basis let us renew our science and go forward with fresh access of power and of love to enhance the comforts and relieve the miseries of mankind.

Whence did this new outlook come? We have already suggested that it drew its origin from the voyages of discovery, from the increased tempo of invention in Western Europe, from the progress of the industrial revolution in England, and from the religious temper of the age. On this last point something more remains to be said.

In Bacon's lifetime centuries of biblical study and scholarship bore fruit in the production of the Authorized Version of the Bible. Apart from the band of learned divines who made this translation, England had at this time in John Selden (1584-1654) her greatest oriental scholar. This scholarship was the fine flower of a wider movement, in full force already with Wyclif in the fourteenth century, through which the English people, acquiring the Scriptures in their own tongue, acquired also the habit of interpreting their own experience in the light of them. Here they found words to express their ideals; hence they drew courage to nerve them in their political and social struggles; here they found the assurance of divine approval and support. The study of the Bible brought them to self-consciousness as a people.

John Milton, who was eleven years old when *The Great Instauration* was published and who was a fervent advocate of its message, will illustrate as well as another the place of the Bible in the English consciousness at this time. Speaking of the Reformation he exclaims: "Then was the sacred Bible sought out of the dusty corners where profane falsehood and neglect had thrown it, the schools opened, divine and human learning raked out of the embers of forgotten tongues." (*Of Reformation in England*, Book I.) He often stresses the primacy of the English in bringing about the Reformation, connecting this with the name of Wyclif and the spread of the Scriptures in the English tongue. This devotion to the Bible bred a conviction of sharing the knowledge of God's purposes which was not without its naïve side. "God is decreeing to begin some great and new period in his church, even to the reforming of reformation itself; what does he then do but reveal himself to his servants, and, as his manner is, first to his Englishmen?" (*Areopagitica.*) The sober Bacon never committed himself to such extravagant expression, but he too had his share of the conviction, founded on the Bible, that he was the chosen instrument of God to work this great reform. It is the key to some puzzling aspects of his work.

His reputation as a bold innovator in science has sometimes obscured Bacon's dependence on the Bible. But the fact is that he always fitted his crusade for the redemption of man into the scheme of Christian theology. The very choice of the word instauration reveals this, especially coupled with his explicit reference to Genesis and his appeal to the oracle from Daniel.

These allusions might be accorded no more than a superficial significance were it not for such passages as that we have already quoted from the conclusion of the Second Book of the *Novum Organum.* Here we find the formal statement of his belief that the effects of the Fall may at least in part be overcome by science. This Christian symbolism is continued in the title *Parasceve* and persists in the *New Atlantis,* where the land itself is called Bensalem and the saintly scientists who direct its destinies constitute The College of the Six Days' Works or Solomon's House.

If in this way we put ourselves at Bacon's point of view, what has been a puzzle to some becomes plain. I refer to Bacon's hostility to Aristotle in particular, to

Plato in a somewhat less degree, and in some degree to almost all the Greeks except Democritus and a few other pre-Socratics. It has been observed that his quarrel seems to be not with their intellectual but with their moral position, but the ground of the quarrel has not been made clear. In the strange writing called *The Masculine Birth of Time*—which it must be admitted is violent and intemperate—he speaks of his concern with Greek philosophy as a pollution.

What did he mean by this? What did he mean when he said about Plato and Aristotle that no denunciation could be adequate to their monstrous guilt (*pro ipsorum sontissimo reatu*)? The answer is simple. He believed that the type of philosophy for which they stood was the great obstacle to a divinely promised revolution in human affairs. They held up the blessing, the blessing which was the subject of Bacon's fervent prayers. The following was found among his papers: "To God the Father, God the Word, God the Spirit, we pour out our humble and burning prayers, that they would be mindful of the miseries of the human race and of this pilgrimage of our life in which we wear out evil days and few, and would unseal again the refreshing fountain of their mercy for the relief of our sufferings." To be held fit to receive this blessing, Bacon believed, it was necessary to reject the false philosophy of the Greeks.

For, however unjustly, Bacon did consider Aristotle and the rest to be in some sense guilty. In the *Refutation of Philosophies* and again in the *De Augmentis* he even compares Aristotle to the anti-Christ. The philosophy of Aristotle is involved in guilt and its punishment is to be fruitless in works. Various passages define the nature of the guilt. In the *De Augmentis* Solomon and Saint Paul are cited to testify that all knowledge is corrupt that is not mixed with love, and the proof of love in philosophy is that it should be designed not for mental satisfaction but for the production of works.

The same theme is the subject of the second of his *Sacred Meditations*. Here his argument is that while the doctrine of Jesus was for the benefit of the soul, all His miracles were for the body. "He restoreth motion to the lame, light to the blind, speech to the dumb, health to the sick, cleanness to the lepers, sound mind to them that were possessed with devils, life to the dead. There was no miracle of judgment, but all of mercy, and all upon the human body."

What, then, precisely was the nature of the sin which had rendered Aristotelianism and so much else of Greek philosophy fruitless for good? It was the sin of intellectual pride, manifested in the presumptuous endeavor to conjure the knowledge of the nature of things out of one's own head instead of seeking it patiently in the Book of Nature. In almost the last thing Bacon published—the Preface to *The History of the Winds* (1623)—he sets forth at length his understanding of the matter. "Without doubt we are paying for the sin of our first parents and imitating it. They wanted to be like Gods; we, their posterity, still more so. We create worlds. We prescribe laws to nature and lord it over her. We want to have all things as suits our fatuity, not as fits the Divine Wisdom, not as they are found in nature. We impose the seal of our image on the creatures and works of God, we do not diligently seek to discover the seal of God on things. Therefore not undeservedly have we again fallen from our dominion over the creation; and, though after the Fall of man some dominion over rebellious nature still remained—to the extent at least that it could be subdued and controlled by true and solid arts—even that we have for the most part forfeited by our pride, because we wanted to be like gods and follow the dictates of our own reason."

His point is clear. False philosophy is a sin of intellectual pride, imitated from our first parents, perpetuated down the ages, and still punished by the loss of dominion over things. But we have not finished our quotation. Writing now at the very end of his life, anxiously concerned to spare no effort for the accomplishment of the purpose which he believed himself to have been put on earth to effect, but with a control of language and emotion which only the years could give, Bacon pours out again his expression of the same conviction which had animated him in *The Masculine Birth of Time:*

"Wherefore, if there be any humility towards the Creator, if there be any reverence and praise of his works; if there be any charity towards men, and zeal to lessen human wants and human sufferings; if there be any love of truth in natural things, any hatred of darkness, any desire to purify the understanding; men are to be entreated again and again that they should dismiss for a while or at least put aside those inconstant and preposterous philosophies, which prefer theses to hypotheses, have led experience captive, and triumphed over the works of God; that they should humbly and with a certain reverence draw near to the book of Creation; that

149

there they should make a stay, that on it they should meditate, and that then washed and clean they should in chastity and integrity turn them from opinion. This is that speech and language which has gone out to all the ends of the earth,* and has not suffered the confusion of Babel; this must men learn, and, resuming their youth, they must become again as little children and deign to take its alphabet into their hands."

The conclusion that emerges from the study of such passages as these is that for Bacon it was still possible in all sincerity to put forward his scientific reform as his own interpretation of Christianity. In the exposition of his scientific purpose which we have just read, the leading ideas are borrowed from the Christian scheme of things and the language is often reminiscent of the Psalms. And as he brings his theology into his science, so he brings his science into his prayers. The Preface to *The History of the Winds* ends with this prayer: "May God the Creator, Preserver, and Restorer of the universe, in accordance with his mercy and his loving-kindness toward man, protect and guide this work both in its ascent to his glory and in its descent to the service of man, through his only Son, God with us." The "ascent to his glory" is the inductive process leading to the highest axioms; the "descent to the service of man" is the deductive process by which science is applied to works. These are the two chief moments of the Baconian scientific process.

This identification of his scientific reform with his Christianity resulted from the actual conditions of England in his day. Bacon championed the new England

* From Psalm xix.

which had been begun by the confiscation of monastic lands and was being completed by the industrial revolution of his day. In his fragment *The True Greatness of Britain*, written about the time James mounted the throne, he describes the kind of England he wants. It was one "whose wealth resteth in the hands of merchants, burghers, tradesmen [i.e., manufacturers], freeholders, farmers in the country, and the like; whereof we have a most evident and present example before our eyes, in our neighbours of the Low Countries, who could never have endured and continued so inestimable and insupportable charges, either by their natural frugality or by their mechanical industry, were it not also that their wealth was dispersed in many hands, and not ingrossed in few; and those hands were not so much of the nobility, but most and generally of inferior conditions." The obstacle to this new bourgeois England was the survival of feudalism; the philosophy of the upholders of feudalism was the Aristotelianism of the Schools. The fight for science in industry was thus associated in Bacon's mind with the reform of philosophy and the reform of religion.

The sharpness of this struggle is evident in the terms and in the tone in which Bacon describes the philosophical tendencies to which he is opposed. "This philosophy, if it be carefully examined, will be found to advance certain points of view which are deliberately designed to cripple enterprise. Such points of view are the opinion that the heat of the sun is a different thing from the heat of fire; or that men can only juxtapose things while nature alone can make them act upon one another. The effect and intention of these arguments is to convince men that

151

nothing really great, nothing by which nature can be commanded and subdued, is to be expected from human art and human labour. Such teachings, if they be justly appraised, will be found to tend to nothing less than a wicked effort to curtail human power over nature and to produce a deliberate and artificial despair. This despair in its turn confounds the promptings of hope, cuts the springs and sinews of industry, and makes men unwilling to put anything to the hazard of trial." (*Novum Organum,* I, 75; *Thoughts and Conclusions,* Spedding and Ellis, III, pp. 592 and 594.)

In the heat of this struggle it is not surprising that Bacon sometimes underestimated the work to be done and overestimated his own powers. In the *Parasceve,* pleading for helpers to gather together the material of the Encyclopedia, he seems to think it not impossible that he could accomplish the work of interpretation single-handed. "So far as the work of the intellect is concerned, I may perhaps successfully accomplish it by my own powers, but the materials for the intellect to work upon are so widely scattered that, to borrow a metaphor from the world of commerce, factors and merchants must seek them out on all sides and import them." But a few years later, in his Preface to *The History of the Winds,* he looks for helpers in the work of the intellect too. "It has occurred to me, likewise, that there are doubtless many wits scattered over Europe, capacious, open, lofty, subtle, solid, and constant." They, if presented with the new Encyclopedia, "will raise much more solid structures" than the old speculative philosophers.

But, with or without helpers, what Bacon was wanting

was a lever to move the world, and this determined the character of his work and the coldness with which it was viewed by his scientific contemporaries. Without adequate knowledge of the particular sciences (for this was beyond the capacity of any one man), he was prepared to try his hand at them one after the other. He had projects in his head by the hundred and undertook investigations by tens. But, while we appreciate the value of his general directions and admire his passionate concern for science in the service of mankind; while we note his considerable degree of success in some investigations (e.g., Heat) and find that even the great Hermann Boerhaave (1668-1738) thought highly of his contribution to medicine; we must also often feel that he was quite out of his depth. We cannot forbear to smile at him puffing his paper windmills round with the help of a pair of bellows and a plentiful lack of mechanical knowledge; or busying himself with the determination of specific gravities without being abreast of what Archimedes had achieved nearly two thousand years before.

The foibles of a great man strike his contemporaries. His greatness is often concealed from them. So it was that William Harvey (1578-1657), the discoverer of the circulation of the blood, who was Bacon's contemporary at the court of King James and attended him professionally, shared the King's low opinion of the *Instauration*. While James delivered himself of the observation that the philosophy of Bacon was "like the peace of God, which passes all understanding," Harvey—speaking, we are told, in derision—said, "He writes philosophy like a Lord Chancellor." Harvey was entitled to his point of view, for he was a faithful disciple of the strict tradition of anatomical and physiological research which stretched from the Hippocratic doctors and the Academy of Alexandria through Galen to Vesalius and his school at Padua. Here Harvey had been trained. Faithful to this tradition and expert in the technique appropriate to his chosen field, Harvey, after years of patient experiment, arrived—not by way of an "indulgence of the intellect" or a "first vintage" but by a rigorous demonstration—at his bit of truth. And this has in fact been the way that most scientists have achieved their results. Harvey had a case against Bacon.

But it takes all sorts to make a world, and Bacon also had a case against Harvey. Harvey was not concerned with building Bensalem in England's green and pleasant land. In his private notes Bacon has recorded the names of certain court physicians he thought capable of entering into the meaning of his plan. The likeliest, he thought, were Sir William Paddy and John Hammond. He does not mention Harvey.

X

The downfall of the Lord Chancellor - The literary activity of the last five years - Death - Editors, biographers, and critics

Francis Bacon had been made Lord Chancellor in January 1618 and Baron Verulam in July of the same year. *The Great Instauration* was published in October 1620. In the following January he was created Viscount St. Albans. He had often repented of his folly in trying to combine the double career of a statesman and a philosopher, but at this time of his life it must sometimes have seemed to him that he had been right after all. His career at court had been crowned with success and, in however imperfect a form, his plan for a revolution in human destiny had been got within the covers of a book and published to the world. His humiliation, however, was at hand. He had tasted success, he was now to taste disgrace.

In the spring of 1621 charges of corruption in his high

office of Chancellor were laid before the bar of the House of Lords. The rumor of them had been in the air for some time, and at first he inclined to treat them with contempt. To the Marquis of Buckingham he wrote: "I know I have clean hands and a clean heart, and I hope a clean house for friends or servants. But Job himself, or whosoever was the justest judge, by such hunting for matters against him as hath been used against me, may for a time seem foul, specially in a time when greatness is the mark and accusation is the game."

This looks like a cry of injured innocence. Yet Bacon knew that he was not innocent and soon admitted it. He was a judge and he was in the habit of accepting presents from litigants. That a gift from a litigant might be innocent nobody would deny. But when does a gift become a bribe? Given at some customary season of gifts as a mark of esteem it may pass as innocent and even be hard to refuse. Given by the successful litigant on the conclusion of a case it is dubious. Is it an admissible token of gratitude for a fair conduct of the case, or a reward for a favorable judgment? A scrupulous man would not entangle himself in such doubts. But, given while judgment is still pending, it is both morally and legally indefensible. The judge may still plead that his judgment was not influenced by the acceptance of the gift and he may even be right, but still he is in an indefensible position. Bacon had accepted gifts under all these circumstances, even the last.

That Bacon had an immense household ruled, by reason of his innumerable preoccupations, with a very loose rein, we know. That gifts might be accepted by his servants without his knowledge seems to be true. But there is a limit to the carelessness that can be excused. Bacon wanted money. His release from straitened circumstances had not meant recovery from debt. Each access of fortune provided security for fresh borrowing. He wanted money and he did not scrutinize too nicely the channels by which it arrived. When it became clear that his accusers intended to press their charge and that the Lords were likely to condemn him, Bacon subjected his conduct to deeper consideration than he had done when he exonerated himself in his private letter to Buckingham, and he penned a confession of guilt. "It resteth therefore that, without fig-leaves, I do ingenuously confess and acknowledge, that having understood the particulars of the charge, not formally from the House but enough to inform my conscience and memory, I find matter sufficient and full, both to move me to desert the defence, and to move your lordships to condemn and censure me." He thought fit also to plead the corruption of the age. "Neither will your lordships forget that there are *vitia temporis* as well as *vitia hominis.*"*

He had condemned himself. The House also condemned him. It is duly reported in their proceedings as follows:

"This High Court (having first summoned him to attend, and having received his excuse of not attending by reason of infirmity and sickness, which he protested was not feigned, or else he would most willingly have attended) doth nevertheless think fit to proceed to judgment; and therefore this High Court doth adjudge:

* Vices of the times as well as vices of the individual.

"1. That the Lord Viscount St. Albans, Lord Chancellor of England, shall undergo fine and ransom of forty thousand pounds.

"2. That he shall be imprisoned in the Tower during the King's pleasure.

"3. That he shall for ever be incapable of any office, place, or employment in the State or Commonwealth.

"4. That he shall never sit in Parliament nor come within the verge of the Court."

The detention in the Tower lasted no longer than a few days, and the fine was eventually remitted by the King. These concessions meant that he could still devote himself to his private ambition. But the fall was complete. We find the ex-Lord Chancellor canvassing unsuccessfully to be made Provost of Eton.

While the trial and judgment were pending, Bacon was physically ill. Documents which he penned at the time testify also to his mental and spiritual distress. He wrote a Last Will and Testament in which he bequeathed his "soul to God above," his "body to be buried obscurely," his "name to the next ages and foreign nations." This is eloquent of his conviction that his public career had been a mistake and might be forgotten by his country, but that his book would live. A prayer he wrote at this time, which Addison said resembled the devotion rather of an angel than a man, ends on the same note. "Besides my innumerable sins, I confess before thee, that I am debtor to thee for the gracious talent of thy gift and graces, which I have neither put into a napkin, nor put it (as I ought) to exchangers, where it might have made best profit; but misspent it in things for which I was least fit; so that I may truly say, my soul hath been a stranger in the course of my pilgrimage."

Recovering his health and his capacity for work, he took heart again for life and passed some typically balanced judgments on his fall. Admitting that he had taken improper presents, he denied that he had ever sold a judgment, and it is not known that any of his judgments were reversed after his fall. He said he was "the justest judge that was in England these fifty years"; but by this he meant to claim only a relative probity, for he admitted the corruption of the age and the need for reform: "It was the justest censure in Parliament that was these two hundred years."

His account with his conscience settled and his health restored, and being at last finally freed from the drudgery of office, he flung himself into his proper business of writing. Within a few months he had completed his *History of Henry VII* (1622). It was his first essay in political history, the only one he had time to complete, and it forms a landmark in modern historiography. The composition is masterly. The writer dominates his material. He gets beneath facts to causes. We seem after a lapse of many centuries to be back again in fifth-century Greece when the art of history was created.

This was followed in November of the same year by what was supposed to be the first monthly instalment of the Encyclopedia, namely *The History of the Winds*. His optimism had again got the better of him. There was no possibility that he could produce twelve volumes a year of the size and quality of the first. True, the second instalment, *The History of Life and Death*,* was only a month late. But it was the last he was destined to complete.

It was not death that interrupted him. He was trying to push forward *The Great Instauration* in all its main parts, and his major effort throughout 1623 was given to Part One. His intention was that this Part should be a work on *The Division of the Sciences*, a sort of map of the intellectual world. So far he had allowed *The Advancement of Learning* to do duty for this part. Now, despairing of completing a new work on the theme, he made up his mind to adapt the *Advancement* to suit the place it must fill. He had it all translated into Latin; he cut out expressions that might offend the ears of Roman Catholic readers on the Continent; he added much new material, so that the original two books now became nine. Thus came into existence the imposing volume known as the *De Augmentis Scientiarum*. The range of the work is immense. The new material is extensive and important. He supervised, where he did not make, the translation. The book bears signs of haste. But it is amazing that it should have been got ready so quickly. It came from the press in October 1623.

The general purpose of the book is to survey the whole field of human knowledge and bring back a report on its achievements and limitations. At the end he draws up a catalogue of the departments of knowledge he finds missing. It contains fifty items from which I select the following as the most significant:

* This was the work that so excited the admiration of Boerhaave.

The *Great Harry*

The Francis Bacon monument in St. Michael's Church, St. Albans

1. Praetergenerations, or freaks in nature.
2. Mechanical history, or the history of inventions.
3. Natural History so arranged as to be a foundation for a philosophy of works.
4. The History of learning.
5. The Philosophy of the Ancient Fables.
6. Primary Philosophy, or a treatise of the common axioms of the sciences.
7. Living Astronomy, which would go beyond the traditional concern with the mere motions of the stars, ignore the imaginary difference between superlunary and sublunary things, and try to arrive at knowledge of the substance of the heavenly bodies by the examination of familiar earthly things.
8. Sane Astrology, or the scientific investigation of the influence exerted on our planet by outside bodies.
9. A collection of the fragments of the pre-Socratics.
10. Metaphysics, or the search for Forms as determined in matter, not abstracted from matter in Plato's way.
11. Natural Magic, or the application of the knowledge of Forms to practice.
12. An inventory of human possessions, designed to guide and encourage man in his pursuit of better things.
13. The Triumphs of man, or a record of the highest mental and physical attainments of humanity, to balance the Miseries of man copiously set forth by philosophers and theologians.
14. Comparative Anatomy, not in the sense of a comparison between men and animals, but a study of the diversities of shape and condition of the vari-

ous parts and organs of the body in different men, as a basis for therapy.

15. On the treatment of diseases pronounced incurable.
16. On the means for rendering death easy to the body.
17. On the prolongation of life.
18. On the substance of the sensible soul, or the natural history of the faculties of reason, imagination, memory, appetite, will.
19. On the difference between sense and perception, "perception" meaning every effect of one body on another which occurs without sensation, like magnetism, or the uniting of two bubbles.
20. Learned Experience (*Experientia literata*), or experiment which does not ascend to axioms.
21. The New Logic, or experimental science which seeks for axioms.
22. A philosophical Grammar, which, going beyond the simple grammars which facilitate the learning of languages, would discuss the various properties of different languages, showing in what points each excelled or failed.
23. The Georgics of the mind, or the Culture of Morals.
24. The Ideal of Universal Justice, in which a specimen is given of the way in which Bacon would have handled the task of making a Digest of the fundamental maxims of the Law.

This extraordinary book demonstrates perhaps more clearly than any other of Bacon's writings the fact that his vision was not limited to the material improvement of man's lot. Here as elsewhere he is himself convinced, and is eager to convince others, that without the determined conquest of man's lost dominion over nature the other things for which he sighs will remain dreams. But he has many proposals also for the improvement of the cultural side of life.

Notable in this connection is his plea for a general History of Learning, a thing that did not yet exist. "Without this," he says, "the history of the world seems to me as the statue of Polyphemus without the eye, that very feature being left out which most marks the spirit and life of the person." As one chapter in this history he urges the collecting of the fragments of the early Greek philosophers and indicates the sources from which the material might be drawn and the principles on which it might be arranged. (Book II, Chapter 4, and Book III, Chapter 4.)

His praise of poetry (Book II, Chapter 13) has in it a rare depth of philosophy. "As the sensible world is inferior in dignity to the rational soul, Poesy seems to bestow upon human nature those things which history denies it. A sound argument may be drawn from Poesy to show that there is agreeable to the spirit of man a more ample greatness, a more perfect order, and a more beautiful variety than it can anywhere (since the Fall) find in nature. So that this Poesy conduces not only to delight but also to magnanimity and morality. Whence it may be fairly thought to partake somewhat of a divine nature; because it raises the mind and carries it aloft, accommodating the shows of things to the desires of the mind, not (like reason and history) buckling and bowing the mind to the nature of things." We have condensed this passage. Those interested in the meaning and function of poetry should go to the original.

Arts ancillary to the literature also receive attention. His plea for Philosophical Grammar, what we now call linguistics, shows profound insight. Witness the incidental remark that though the accentuation of *words* has been exquisitely handled, the accentuation of *sentences* has entirely escaped notice. He rejects a proposal for phonetic spelling on the ground that pronunciation is always changing.

For the student of Bacon's philosophy of nature the most important portion of the *De Augmentis* is Book III, Chapters 4, 5, and 6. He here gives us a necessary clue to the interpretation of his works when he says that he prefers, out of respect for antiquity, to stick to the traditional vocabulary, but that we must expect the words to bear new meanings which will be clear from the context. Here he was unduly optimistic, for his use of the traditional terms in new senses has produced problems of interpretation with which we cannot adequately concern ourselves in a short introductory book. He is explicit, however, on one all-important point, namely, that he uses "Metaphysics," not in the Platonic sense but to describe a portion of Natural Philosophy. Plato, he says, tried to apprehend Forms abstracted from matter, "whence it came that he turned aside to theological speculations, wherewith all his natural philosophy is infected and polluted." If, by his preference for the traditional vocabulary, Bacon described his own philosophy also as a quest for Forms, he makes clear that the Forms must be found in matter and the proof that one has found them is the power to produce material effects. In the *Novum Organum* (II, 17) he had already given emphatic warning that he did not use the word Forms in any sense to which men had been accustomed. "I never allow myself to be drawn away from things themselves and the active control of them. Accordingly, if I say 'rarity does not belong to the Form of heat,' all I mean is that it is possible to make a dense body hot."

We shall conclude with an ethical passage (Book VII, Chapter 1) which is all-important for the understanding of the man. In it he contrasts the claims of the private and the common good. He first endeavors to prove that even in inorganic nature there is a law which obliges the individual thing to submit to the claims of the collectivity. But we shall pass by this curious speculation and confine our attention to human society. To illustrate the supremacy of the claims of the community over the individual he chooses an example first from pagan antiquity. This is the noble saying of Pompey, when a public duty demanded a voyage which imperiled his life: "It is needful that I go, not that I live." Next, he illustrates the Christian devotion to this principle, and cites the instance of certain saints of God, who, "in an ecstasy of charity and infinite feeling of communion," wished themselves to be erased out of the Book of Life rather than that any of the brethren should not obtain salvation. Then, characteristically, he uses this principle of the supremacy of the public good to condemn Aristotle. "It decides the question touching the preferment of the contemplative or active life, and decides it against Aristotle. For all the reasons which he gives in favour of the contemplative

165

life respect private good, and the pleasure and dignity of a man's self; in which respects no question but the contemplative life has the pre-eminence. . . . But men must know that in this theatre of man's life it is reserved only for God and Angels to be lookers-on."

It is to this interpretation of his public duty we owe it that Francis Bacon wrote no more books. The only other thing he published in the two and a half years still left to him was the third (revised and much enlarged) edition of the *Essays*. For the rest he busied himself heaping together indiscriminately from secondary sources the materials for his *Encyclopedia* or *Natural and Experimental History*. To this he alludes in the opening of Book VII of the *De Augmentis* from which we have just quoted, in a passage addressed to the King. "For myself, most excellent king, I may truly say that both in this present work, and in those I intend to publish hereafter, I often advisedly and deliberately throw aside the dignity of my name and wit (if such thing be) in my endeavour to advance human interests; and being one that should properly perhaps be an architect in philosophy and the sciences, I turn common labourer, hodman, anything that is wanted; taking upon myself the burden and execution of many things which must needs be done, and which others through an inborn pride shrink from and decline."

It was while busying himself in what might be described as a hodman's job in the construction of the edifice of scientific knowledge that Bacon contracted the illness that proved fatal. At this time he was living again in his old quarters in Gray's Inn, "for quiet," as he said, "and the better to hold out"—alluding to his reduction by his disgrace to comparative poverty. The problem of Heat and Cold had always fascinated him both theoretically and for its practical applications. The effect of cold in delaying putrefaction was on the list of his problems to be investigated. On a cold day towards the end of March 1626 he found himself driving over snow-covered ground near Highgate * and decided not to waste the opportunity. The old man descended from his carriage, purchased a hen from a cottage woman and helped stuff it with snow. He was immediately sensible of having taken a chill and sought the hospitality of Lord Arundel, one of whose houses lay conveniently near. The master was not at home but the servants admitted him. It seems that their sense of the importance of their guest dictated a foolish decision. Only the best bed would do, but it was not adequately warmed and aired. Bacon at first was well enough to write a gracious and lively letter of thanks to his absent host in which he betrays no awareness that his illness is serious. He describes the experiment with the hen and cheerfully compares his exposure of himself to the cold in the interest of scientific truth with the determination of the elder Pliny to see Vesuvius in eruption from close quarters—a determination which cost him his life. But, whether because the bed was damp or because the original chill was worse than he had thought, the comparison with Pliny proved only too apt. Bacon was seized with bronchitis and died early on Easter Sunday morning, April 9th, 1626.

His comparison of himself to Pliny may be extended to more than the manner of their deaths. Pliny, like Ba-

* A northern suburb of London, now a part of the Metropolitan area.

con, had striven to make knowledge useful to man. Precisely for this reason Bacon had described him in the *De Augmentis* (Book II) as "the only person who ever undertook a Natural History according to the dignity of it." Bacon had the fortune often to say better things about himself than any later biographer has been able to do. So it is with this comparison of himself to Pliny. He could not want a better epitaph than that which links him with the old Roman as one who saw the true dignity of science in its usefulness. What deathbed could be more appropriate for one who as a Cambridge undergraduate not yet fifteen years old had turned in disgust from the prevailing philosophy because it was fruitless in works for the benefit of the life of man? In one way or another he had fought for that conviction through the remaining fifty years of his life. And even now, after three hundred years, if his name is still remembered it is simply for this, that with all his splendid powers of heart and mind he fought to render intelligible and acceptable the opinion that the pursuit of truth in science is inseparable from the improvement of our human lot.

Bacon was sixty-five years old when he died. His intellectual vigor, however, seemed unimpaired and he had just achieved that freedom from public duties for which he had sighed so long. Is it legitimate, then, to think that he died too young and that his best work, perhaps, still remained to be done? I think we may be confident that he had really accomplished his task and that he could have added nothing essential to what he had already done. He was not likely to make any important addition to any branch of experimental science. He had lived long enough to show that his genius did not lie in this field, and this work could well be allowed to pass into younger and more competent hands.

But neither was he likely to effect any great improvement in the general theoretical foundation of his doctrine on the world of nature and of man. Human knowledge is a slow growth and even the most outstanding thinkers bring only a little more light and order into the darkness and confusion that surround us. When they first hold up their torch we are dazzled by its brilliance. Afterwards, we see that the circle of light has only been extended a little.

Bacon's philosophy was, in fact, full of contradictions. We shall mention three. First, he made an absolute division between divine and natural knowledge. He gave splendid encouragement and direction for advancing natural knowledge, but he taught that divine truth should be accepted without criticism from the Bible. He did not see that this is impossible. For people do not agree on what is to be included under the name of divine truth, and Bacon did nothing to suggest either a rational criterion of such truth or an authority to decide and impose it. His disciple Thomas Hobbes (1588-1679), seeing this difficulty, recommended that the State should fix the creed of the subjects and enforce it. Bacon would have shrunk from this solution. But himself he had none.

Secondly, he accepted a self-contradictory view of the human soul. Sometimes he seems prepared to deduce all the intellectual and moral faculties of the human soul, as he does with the souls of animals, from the primary motion of the atoms. At other times he insists that there is a distinction not of degree but of kind between the human and the animal soul, and says that this is because the distinctively human soul has a divine origin. It is the breath of God, a doctrine he derived from Genesis ii, 7, where it is said that "God breathed into man's nostrils the breath of life, and man became a living soul." It is difficult to understand how these two parts of the soul manage to form a unity, or where precisely Bacon proposed to draw the line between them.

A third contradiction arises in his view of the history of science. On the one hand there is his doctrine of the existence, in some remote antiquity, of a higher state of human wisdom reflected in the ancient fables. On the other there is his much-loved doctrine that modern times are wiser than the old, since antiquity was really the youth of the world.

These and other contradictions impeded the further development of his thought, and it would be idle to fancy that Bacon could have done anything to remove them. As Bacon himself well knew, and has taught us to understand, knowledge is the birth of time, and the kind of contradictions we have been discussing do not admit of any ready-made solutions. If we are interested in the problems Bacon left unresolved, we have no recourse but to study the whole development of science and philosophy in the three hundred years since his death. The growth of the social sciences, the growth of history, the development of archeology and of anthropology, the emergence of biblical criticism as part of that general history of learning for which Bacon pleaded, the development of the evolutionary theory of the origin of species, and much more besides, provide such answer as can yet be given to the problems Bacon left unresolved. Love and admiration for great figures of the past must not blind us to the fact that knowledge is a living, moving thing and that no man, however great, can escape the limitations of his time.

It remains to say a few words of the history of Baconian scholarship: how his writings all came to be published and collected, and how they have fared at the hands of editors, critics, and commentators.

In spite of the immense pains he took with the expression of his ideas, most of what Bacon himself published during his life bears manifest signs of haste and improvisation. Two things, the *Essays* and the *Wisdom of the Ancients,* are completely matured and polished. The *Advancement* was somewhat hastily written and still more hastily expanded and translated into the *De Augmentis. The Great Instauration,* though most carefully elaborated in some of its parts, is as a whole disjointed. We have seen that at the end of Book I of the Logic Bacon announces that he does not intend to finish it, while at the end of Book II he confidently anticipates the completion of the work.

The condition of the published work prepares us to understand what the material he left unpublished was like. It too is perfected in parts but disjointed as a whole—the work of a man who had too many irons in the fire. First there were the half-finished projects on which he was engaged when he died. Then there was the mass of deliberately unpublished papers, prepared either for private circulation or simply as tentative drafts. Some of these are among the best things he did, but it remained for his editors to sort them out and publish them. It must be remembered, too, that his writings were not only scientific. There were ethical, political, historical, and legal writings. There were prayers, meditations, private diaries, a confession of faith, and a collection of apophthegms, not to speak of correspondence.

Fortunately his able and devoted secretary Dr. Rawley charged himself with preserving for posterity all that he could of the fruit of his master's mind. He published promptly (in 1627) the unfinished utopia, the *New Atlantis*, as an appendix to the large collection of material for the Encyclopedia called *Sylva Sylvarum*. The latter is an industrious but indiscriminate compilation—Bacon doing hodman's work. Of all his writings it is the one that could best be spared. The former, with its picture of the humane and scientific ideal society of which he dreamed, is indispensable to the student of Bacon's mind and spirit. Further publications by Rawley of Bacon's writings continued to come from the press at intervals till 1661.

A great bulk of Baconian manuscripts had, however, made their way to Holland. Bacon had appointed as one of his literary executors a Mr. Bosvile (later Sir William Boswell) who was soon made agent with the United Provinces and took up residence at The Hague. Thither the manuscripts followed him. It may well be that some of these were lost. However in 1653 a Dutch publisher, Isaac Gruter, brought out a collection of nineteen philosophical pieces in Latin. This contains, among much else of great value, the brilliant *Thoughts and Conclusions*, which is an earlier draft of the first book of the *Novum*

Organum, but retains an independent interest. New material also came to light from other sources, the most important being published in Tenison's *Baconiana* in 1679.

Meanwhile the enterprise of producing collected editions had begun. Confining ourselves to English productions, there are three early editions to be mentioned—by Blackbourne, 1730; Birch, 1763; Montagu, 1825-34. But these were superseded about the middle of the nineteenth century, when three men, all products of Bacon's own university and college (Trinity, Cambridge), decided to bring fresh order into the immense material now assembled. The men were Robert Leslie Ellis (1817-59), James Spedding (1808-81), and Douglas Denon Heath (1811-97). They proposed to break the material up into the following main divisions: (1) Philosophical Works, (2) Literary Works, (3) Professional (i.e., legal) Works. Ellis was to handle the philosophical, Spedding the literary, and Heath the professional works. The project was one of great importance, for Bacon had long been a world figure, whose chief writings had been translated not only into the languages of Europe but in part even into Sanskrit, whence it was hoped his ideas would penetrate into the daughter languages of the Indian subcontinent.

For these, as for all previous editors, the philosophical works and remains constituted the main interest and problem. These they subdivided into: (1) Writings which actually formed part of *The Great Instauration;* (2) Writings originally intended for this purpose but superseded or thrown aside; (3) Works connected with the plan but but never directly included in it. It is an excellent arrangement with one grave disadvantage—it obscures the historical order of composition.

The project encountered one great setback. Ellis, a man of marked philosophical capacity and solid learning, having undertaken in 1846 to edit the philosophical works, was stricken down with rheumatic fever in 1847. He had made a fundamental contribution to the interpretation of Bacon's thought in the short time his health permitted. It was long before he could make up his mind to abandon his share of the work. But in 1853 it fell to James Spedding to add Ellis's part of the common task to his own. Not only did Spedding carry this burden, but when the seven volumes were at length through the press he proceeded at once to edit another seven under the title *The Letters and the Life*. The fourteen volumes, which came from the press from 1857 to 1874, constitute the greatest monument so far erected to the memory of Francis Bacon. The two men who have best served Bacon's memory are Rawley and Spedding. Each devoted his life to the work. Each was a judicious critic as well as an enthusiastic admirer. The quality of their admiration is high testimony to the man they loved.

We have shown from his writings that Bacon's interest went beyond a reform of logic and was aimed at the transformation of the material conditions of life. This has not always been recognized or allowed its due place in the story of his life. The point was brilliantly made by Macaulay in his provocative and often misleading *Essay on Bacon* (1837). It was given more precise definition by Marx in a footnote to *Capital* (1867) where he says of Bacon and Descartes that "they anticipated an alteration in the form of production, and the practical subjugation of nature by man, as a result of the altered mode of thought." Recent inquirers into the life of the times—whether economic historians like Nef (*Industry and Government in France and England*, 1540-1640) or historians of opinion like R. K. Merton (*Science in Seventeenth Century England*, in *Osiris*, vol. IV, 1938)—help us to understand the social connections of Bacon's thought. There was more truth in Harvey's gibe than he knew when he said that Bacon wrote philosophy like a Lord Chancellor. All Bacon's thought has the unbookish tang of a man who draws up projects for execution rather than writes books to be read.

This, however, is just the quality that is obscured by academic editors. Bacon meditated on his project all his life and when at last he had sufficiently matured it he announced it to the world in dramatic style. He called it *The Great Instauration*. The title seems to hum with life and action. It was a plan, as the author explained, for restoring man's dominion over nature. But editors rarely edit this plan. They prefer to concentrate on the logical aspect of Bacon's work and edit that portion of his work called the *Novum Organum*. Bacon appears between Aristotle and John Stuart Mill as a deviser of rules of thinking. In fact he stopped devising such rules before he had accomplished more than a small portion of his plan, asserting that rules for investigation could not be properly laid down beforehand but must be worked out in the process of investigation itself. The essential thing about Bacon is that he was more than a logician. But the student can hardly find this out. What he knows is that

Kitchin in 1855, Brewer in 1856, Fowler in 1878 and again in 1889, edited the *Novum Organum.* He is told that this is Bacon's most important book, which is true. But he hardly realizes that Bacon himself never published such a book separately, but only as part of *The Great Instauration.*

It must be understood that these words are not intended to decry the solid merits of all these editions. Fowler's second edition is, in fact, the most elaborate study in existence of any portion of Bacon's work and it is indispensable, a treasury of accurate and reliable information. But the title, not to speak of many misleading indications in the text, fixes the character of the work. The ringing challenge of *The Great Instauration* is muffled under the academic cloak of the *Novum Organum.*

The eclipse of Bacon, the reformer of the material conditions of human life, under the academic figure of Bacon, the reformer of the rules of induction, has ruined Baconian scholarship in England. In the former capacity Bacon is the man of his age, easily recognizable as the herald of the industrial revolution, who foresaw the possibility and the consequences of the application of science to industry and pleaded with his countrymen and with the world to stretch their moral and intellectual capacities to meet the new challenge. As a logician his claim to greatness is dubious. Macaulay, detesting that philosophy which makes a boast of its uselessness, could write: "From the cant of this philosophy, a philosophy meanly proud of its own unprofitableness, it is delightful to turn to the lessons of the great English teacher." But when Bacon's tercentenary arrived the logicians were in the ascendant and they could make nothing of Bacon's claim to greatness. C. D. Broad (*The Philosophy of Francis Bacon*, Cambridge, 1926), considered "only his claims to be the Father of Inductive Philosophy" and arrived at the inevitable conclusion: "The actual course which science has taken has been influenced little if at all by his writings." A. E. Taylor (*Francis Bacon*, in *Proceedings of the British Academy*, 1926), concentrated on the theory of Forms, which Ellis [*] had rightly characterized as an extraneous part of Bacon's system, and came to the paradoxical conclusion that "for all his personal want of mathematical equipment" Bacon's true place was as a connecting link between "the two great mathematical metaphysicians of the ancient and modern world, Plato and Leibnitz." To complete the inappropriateness of this description, Taylor only needed to remind us that, as well as being ignorant of mathematics, Bacon proposed to abolish metaphysics in Plato's sense.

Recent contributions from the United States have been more helpful. Charles T. Harrison (*Bacon, Hobbes, Boyle and the Ancient Atomists*, Harvard Studies in Philosophy and Literature, vol. 15) amply proves his point that the influence of Atomism on Bacon had been underrated. Fulton Anderson in a new full-length study (*The Philosophy of Francis Bacon*, 1948) corrects the one great weakness of the Spedding classification of the Philosophical writings by analyzing them all in chronological order. He has produced important results, putting the whole question of the detail of Bacon's criticism of the Greeks

[*] See the General Preface to the Philosophical Works, ed. of Spedding and Ellis, vol. I, pp. 21-67.

on a sound scholarly basis. His book, which is for the specialist, will long influence Baconian studies.

Among older books readers may be glad of some guidance. Those I have found best are Spedding's *The Life and Times of Lord Bacon* (London, 1870), Fowler's *Bacon* (London, 1881), and the article *Francis Bacon* by Robert Adamson in the Encyclopedia Britannica, 9th edition. To these may be added Mary Sturt's lively and perceptive *Francis Bacon* (London, 1932).

Appendix A

GOD BLESS THEE, my son; I will give thee the greatest jewel I have. For I will impart unto thee, for the love of God and men, a relation of the true state of Solomon's House. Son, to make you know the true state of Solomon's House, I will keep this order. First, I will set forth unto you the end of our foundation. Secondly, the preparations and instruments we have for our works. Thirdly, the several employments and functions whereto our fellows are assigned. And fourthly, the ordinances and rites which we observe.

The End of our Foundation is the knowledge of Causes, and secret motions of things; and the enlarging of the bounds of Human Empire, to the effecting of all things possible.

The Preparations and Instruments are these. We have large and deep caves of several depths: the deepest are sunk 600 fathom: and some of them are digged and made under great hills and mountains: so that if you reckon together the depth of the hill and the depth of the cave, they are (some of them) above three miles deep. For we find that the depth of a hill, and the depth of a cave from the flat, is the same thing; both remote alike from the sun and heaven's beams, and from the open air. These caves we call the Lower Region. And we use them for all coagulations, indurations, refrigerations, and conservations of bodies. We use them likewise for the imitation of natural mines; and the producing also of new artificial metals, by compositions and materials which we use, and lay there for many years. We use them also sometimes, (which may seem strange,) for curing of some diseases, and for prolongation of life in some hermits that choose to live there, well accommodated of all things necessary; and indeed live very long; by whom also we learn many things.

We have burials in several earths, where we put diverse cements, as the Chinese do their porcelain. But we have them in greater varieties, and some of them more fine. We have also great variety of composts, and soils, for the making of the earth fruitful.

We have high towers; the highest about half a mile in height; and some of them likewise set upon high mountains: so that the vantage of the hill with the tower is in the highest of them three miles at least. And these places we call the Upper Region: accounting the air between the high places and the low, as a Middle Region. We use these towers, according to their several heights and situations, for insolation, refrigeration, conservation; and for the view of divers meteors; as winds, rain, snow, hail; and some of the fiery meteors also. And upon them, in some places, are dwellings of hermits, whom we visit sometimes, and instruct what to observe.

We have great lakes, both salt and fresh, whereof we have use for the fish and fowl. We use them also for burials of some natural bodies: for we find a difference in things buried in earth or in air below the earth, and things buried in water. We have also pools, of which some do strain fresh water into salt. We have also some rocks in the midst of the sea, and some bays upon the shore, for some works wherein is required the air and vapor of the sea. We have likewise violent streams and cataracts, which serve us for many motions; and likewise engines for multiplying and enforcing of winds, to set also on going diverse motions.

We have also a number of artificial wells and fountains, made in imitation of the natural sources and baths; as tincted upon vitriol, sulphur, steel, brass, lead, nitre, and other minerals. And again we have little wells for infusions of many things, where the waters take the virtue quicker and better than in vessels or basons. And amongst them we have a water which we call Water of Paradise, being, by that we do to it, made very sovereign for health, and prolongation of life.

We have also great and spacious houses, where we imitate and demonstrate meteors; as snow, hail, rain, some artificial rains of bodies and not of water, thunders, lightnings; also generations of bodies in air; as frogs, flies, and divers others.

We have also fair and large baths, of several mixtures,

for the cure of diseases, and the restoring of man's body from arefaction; and others for the confirming of it in strength of sinews, vital parts, and the very juice and substance of the body.

We have also large and various orchards and gardens, wherein we do not so much respect beauty, as variety of ground and soil, proper for divers trees and herbs; and some very spacious, where trees and berries are set whereof we make divers kinds of drinks, besides the vineyards. In these we practise likewise all conclusions of grafting and inoculating, as well of wild-trees as fruit-trees, which produceth many effects. And we make (by art) in the same orchards and gardens, trees and flowers to come earlier or later than their seasons; and to come up and bear more speedily than by their natural course they do. We make them also by art greater much than their nature; and their fruit greater and sweeter and of differing taste, smell, color, and figure, from their nature. And many of them we so order, as they become of medicinal use.

We have also means to make divers plants rise by mixtures of earths without seeds; and likewise to make divers new plants, differing from the vulgar; and to make one tree or plant turn into another.

We have also parks and inclosures of all sorts of beasts and birds, which we use not only for view or rareness, but likewise for dissections and trials; that thereby we may take light what may be wrought upon the body of men. Wherein we find many strange effects; as continuing life in them, though divers parts, which you account vital, be perished and taken forth; resuscitating of some that seem dead in appearance; and the like. We try also all poisons and other medicines upon them, as well of chirurgery as physic. By art likewise, we make them greater or taller than their kind is; and contrariwise barren and not generative. Also we make them differ in color, shape, activity, many ways. We find means to make commixtures and copulations of different kinds; which have produced many new kinds, and them not barren, as the general opinion is. We make a number of kinds of serpents, worms, flies, fishes, of putrefaction; whereof some are advanced (in effect) to be perfect creatures, like beasts or birds; and have sexes, and do propagate. Neither do we this by chance, but we know beforehand of what matter and commixture what kind of those creatures will arise.

We have also particular pools, where we make trials upon fishes, as we have said before of beasts and birds.

We have also places for breed and generation of those kinds of worms and flies which are of special use; such as are with you your silk-worms and bees.

I will not hold you long with recounting of our brewhouses, bake-houses, and kitchens, where are made divers drinks, breads, and meats, rare and of special effects. Wines we have of grapes; and drinks of other juice of fruits, of grains, and of roots; and of mixtures with honey, sugar, manna, and fruits dried and decocted. Also of the tears or woundings of trees; and of the pulp of canes. And these drinks are of several ages, some to the age or last of forty years. We have drinks also brewed with several herbs, and roots, and spices; yea with several fleshes, and white meats; whereof some of the drinks are such, as they are in effect meat and drink both; so that divers, especially in age, do desire to live with them, with little or no meat or bread.

And above all, we strive to have drinks of extreme thin parts, to insinuate into the body, and yet without all biting, sharpness, or fretting; insomuch as some of them put upon the back of your hand will, with a little stay, pass through to the palm, and yet taste mild to the mouth. We have also waters which we ripen in that fashion, as they become nourishing; so that they are indeed excellent drink; and many will use no other. Breads we have of several grains, roots, and kernels; yea and some of flesh and fish dried; with divers kinds of leavenings and seasonings: so that some do extremely move Appetites; some do nourish so, as divers do live of them, without any other meat; who live very long. So for meats, we have some of them so beaten and made tender and mortified, yet without all corrupting, as a weak heat of the stomach will turn them into good chylus, as well as a strong heat would meat otherwise prepared. We have some meats also and breads and drinks, which taken by men enable them to fast long after; and some other, that used make the very flesh of men's bodies sensibly more hard and tough, and their strength far greater than otherwise it would be.

We have dispensatories, or shops of medicines. Wherein you may easily think, if we have such variety of plants and living creatures more than you have in Europe, (for we know what you have,) the simples, drugs, and ingredients of medicines, must likewise be in so much the greater variety. We have them likewise of divers ages, and long fermentations. And for their preparations, we have not only all manner of exquisite distillations and separations, and especially by gentle heats and percolations through divers strainers, yea and substances; but also exact forms of composition, whereby they incorporate almost, as they were natural simples.

We have also divers mechanical arts, which you have not; and stuffs made by them; as papers, linen, silks, tissues; dainty works of feathers of wonderful lustre; excellent dyes, and many others; and shops likewise, as well for such as are not brought into vulgar use amongst us as for those that are. For you must know that of the things before recited, many of them are grown into use throughout the kingdom; but yet if they did flow from our invention, we have of them also for patterns and principals.

We have also furnaces of great diversities, and that keep great diversity of heats: fierce and quick; strong and constant; soft and mild; blown, quiet, dry, moist and the like. But above all we have heats, in imitation of the sun's and heavenly bodies' heats, that pass divers inequalities, and (as it were) orbs, progresses, and returns, whereby we produce admirable effects. Besides, we have heats of dungs; and of bellies and maws of living creatures, and of their bloods and bodies; and of hays and herbs laid up moist; of lime unquenched; and such like. Instruments also which generate heat only by motion. And farther, places for strong insolations; and again, places under the earth, which by nature or art yield heat. These divers heats we use, as the nature of the operation which we intend requireth.

We have also perspective-houses, where we make demonstrations of all lights, and radiations; and of all colors; and out of things uncolored and transparent, we can represent unto you all several colors; not in rainbows, as it is in gems and prisms, but of themselves single. We represent also all multiplications of light, which we carry to great distance, and make so sharp as to discern small points and lines; also all colorations of light: all delusions and deceits of the sight, in figures, magnitudes, motions, colors; all demonstrations of shadows. We find also divers means yet unknown to you, of producing of light originally from divers bodies. We procure means of seeing objects afar off; as in the heaven and remote places; and represent things near as afar off; and things afar off as near; making feigned distances. We have also helps for the sight, far above spectacles and glasses in use. We have also glasses and means, to see small and minute bodies perfectly and distinctly; as the shapes and colors of small flies and worms, grains and flaws in gems which cannot otherwise be seen; observations in urine and blood, not otherwise to be seen. We make artificial rain-bows, halos, and circles about light. We represent also all manner of reflexions, refractions, and miltiplications of visual beams of objects.

We have also precious stones of all kinds, many of them of great beauty, and to you unknown; crystals likewise; and glasses of divers kinds; and amongst them some of metals vitrificated, and other materials besides those of which you make glass. Also a number of fossils, and imperfect minerals, which you have not. Likewise loadstones of prodigious virtue; and other rare stones, both natural and artificial.

We have also sound-houses, where we practise and demonstrate all sounds, and their generation. We have harmonies which you have not, of quarter-sounds, and lesser slides of sounds. Divers instruments of music likewise to you unknown, some sweeter than any you have; together with bells and rings that are dainty and sweet. We represent small sounds as great and deep; likewise great sounds extenuate and sharp; we make divers tremblings and warblings of sounds, which in their original are entire. We represent and imitate all articulate sounds and letters, and the voices and notes of beasts and birds. We have certain helps which set to the ear do further the hearing greatly. We have also divers strange and artificial echoes, reflecting the voice many times and as it were tossing it; and some that give back the voice louder than it came; some shriller, and some deeper; yea some rendering the voice differing in the letters or articulate sound from that they receive. We have also means to convey sounds in trunks and pipes, in strange lines and distances.

We have also perfume-houses; wherewith we join also practises of taste. We multiply smells, which may seem strange. We imitate smells, making all smells to breath out of other mixtures than those that give them. We make divers imitations of taste likewise, so that they will deceive any man's taste. And in this house we contain also a confiture-house, where we make all sweet-meats, dry and moist, and divers pleasant wines, milks, broths, and sallets, in far greater variety than you have.

We have also engine-houses, where are prepared engines and instruments for all sorts of motions. There we imitate and practise to make swifter motions than any you have, either out of your muskets or any engine that you have; and to make them and multiply them more easily, and with small force, by wheels and other means: and to make them stronger, and more violent than yours are; exceeding your greatest cannons and basilisks. We represent also ordnance and instruments of war, and engines of all kinds; and likewise new mixtures and compositions of gun-powder, wildfires burning in water, and unquenchable. Also fire-works of all variety both for pleasure and use. We imitate also flights of birds; we have some degrees of flying in the air; we have ships and boats for going under water, and brooking of seas; also swimming-girdles and supporters. We have divers curious clocks; and other like motions of return, and some perpetual motions. We imitate also motions of living creatures, by images of men, beasts, birds, fishes, and serpents. We have also a great number of other various motions, strange for equality, fineness, and subtilty.

We have also a mathematical house, where are represented all instruments, as well of geometry as astronomy, exquisitely made.

We have also houses of deceits of the senses; where we represent all manner of feats of juggling, false apparitions, impostures, and illusions; and their fallacies. And surely you will easily believe that we that have so many things truly natural which induce admiration, could in a world of particulars deceive the senses, if we would disguise those things and labour to make them seem more miraculous. But we do hate all impostures and lies: insomuch as we have severely forbidden it to all our fellows, under pain of ignominy and fines, that they do not shew any natural work or thing, adorned or swelling; but only pure as it is, and without all affectation of strangeness.

These are (my son) the riches of Solomon's House.

For the several employments and offices of our fellows; we have twelve that sail into foreign countries, under the names of other nations, (for our own we conceal;) who bring us the books, and abstracts, and patterns of experiments of all other parts. These we call Merchants of Light.

We have three that collect the experiments which are in all books. These we call Depredators.

We have three that collect the experiments of all mechanical arts; and also of liberal sciences; and also of practises which are not brought into arts. These we call Mystery-men.

We have three that try new experiments, such as themselves think good. These we call Pioners of Miners.

We have three that draw the experiments of the former four into titles and tables, to give the better light for the drawing of observations and axioms out of them. These we call Compilers.

We have three that bend themselves, looking into the experiments of their fellows, and cast about how to draw out of them things of use and practise for man's life, and knowledge as well for works as for plain demonstration of causes, means of natural divinations, and the easy and clear discovery of the virtues and parts of bodies. These we call Dowry-men or Benefactors.

Then after divers meetings and consults of our whole number, to consider of the former labours and collections, we have three that take care, out of them, to direct new experiments, of a higher light, more penetrating into nature than the former. These we call Lamps.

We have three others that do execute the experiments so directed, and report them. These we call Inoculators.

Lastly, we have three that raise the former discoveries by experiments into greater observations, axioms, and aphorisms. These we call Interpreters of Nature.

We have also, as you must think, novices and apprentices, that the succession of the former employed men do not fail; besides a great number of servants and attendants, men and women. And this we do also: we have consultations, which of the inventions and experiences which we have discovered shall be published, and which not: and take all an oath of secrecy, for the concealing of those which we think fit to keep secret: though some of those we do reveal sometimes to the state, and some not.

For our ordinances and rites: we have two very long and fair galleries: in one of these we place patterns and samples of all manner of the more rare and excellent inventions: in the other we place the statua's of all principal inventors. There we have the statua of your Columbus, that discovered the West Indies: also the inventor of ships: your monk that was the inventor of ordnance and of gunpowder: the inventor of music: the inventor of letters: the inventor of printing: the inventor of observations of astronomy: the inventor of works in metal: the inventor of glass: the inventor of silk of the worm: the inventor of wine: inventor of corn and bread: the inventor of sugars: and all these by more certain tradition than you have. Then have we divers inventors of our own, of excellent works; which since you have not seen, it were too long to make descriptions of them; and besides, in the right understanding of those descriptions you might easily err. For upon every invention of value we erect a statua to the inventor, and give him a liberal and honourable reward. These statua's are some of brass; some of marble and touchstone; some of cedar and other special woods gilt and adorned: some of iron; some of silver; some of gold.

We have certain hymns and services, which we say daily, of laud and thanks to God for his marvellous works: and forms of prayers, imploring his aid and blessing for the illumination of our labours, and the turning of them into good and holy uses.

Lastly, we have circuits or visits of divers principal cities of the kingdom; where, as it cometh to pass, we do publish such new profitable inventions as we think good. And we do also declare natural divinations of diseases, plagues, swarms of hurtful creatures, scarcity, tempests, earth-quakes, great inundations, comets, temperature of the year, and divers other things; and we give counsel thereupon what the people shall do for the prevention and remedy of them.

And when he had said this, he stood up; and I, as I had been taught, kneeled down, and he laid his right hand upon my head, and said; God bless thee, my son, and God bless this relation, which I have made. I give thee leave to publish it for the good of other nations; for we here are in God's bosom, a land unknown.

Appendix B

Notes to the illustrations

Frontispiece. A full account of this portrait is given in the introduction to the first volume of the *Works of Francis Bacon* by Spedding and Ellis. The original engraving was published almost certainly in the first half of 1618.

The portraits of Francis Bacon as a boy and of his mother and father are photographs of the life-sized colored terra-cotta busts now in the possession of the present Lord Verulam. The physical resemblance of Francis to his mother is striking.

Sir Nicholas's house at Gorhambury is described at length by H. M. M. Lane in the *Transactions* of the St. Albans and Hertfordshire Architectural and Archaeological Society, 1932, and by J. C. Rogers in the same journal of the year 1933. Both articles are full of valuable and unusual information. The house, the third Sir Nicholas built, was in construction from 1563–68. That is to say, it was completed when Francis was seven. As his father took a lively interest in the progress of the work it is certain that Francis early had the chance to acquaint himself with a great number of trades—sawyers, carpenters, masons, bricklayers, joiners, plasterers, glaziers, paviers, plumbers, etc. There were gardens also filled with rare plants. In Francis Bacon's notebooks are many references to Gorhambury and its gardens.

The frontispiece to *The Great Instauration* is described in the text (pp. 25-26). Here it must be mentioned that the influence of Gorhambury is plainly expressed in the design. In the great hall at Gorhambury on the wall over the table was a painting of Ceres teaching the sowing of grain with the legend *Moniti Meliora*. These words reappear in the scroll at the bottom of the frontispiece. Nothing could be more eloquent of the influence of his father on Francis.

The *Great Harry* represents an Elizabethan battleship of about 1587. It is the kind of ship described by Bacon in his *History of the Winds*.

The monument in St. Michael's Church was erected by one of his secretaries, Sir Thomas Meautys. Rawley says that it "represents his full portraiture in the posture of studying." The inscription was composed by Sir Henry Wotton. I here reproduce it in full with translation:

Franciscus Bacon. Baro de Verulā.
Sti. Albni. Vicms.
seu notioribus titulis
Scientiarum Lumem. Facundiae Lex
sic sedebat.

Qui postquam omnia naturalis sapientiae
et civilis arcana evolvisset

naturae decretum explevit.
Composita Solvantur.
Ano. Dni. MDCXXVI
Aetats. LXVI.

Tanti Viri
mem.
Thomas Meautys
Superstitis Cultor
Defuncti Admirator
H. P.

Francis Bacon, Baron of Verulam,
Viscount St. Albans
or by more conspicuous titles
of Science the Light, of Eloquence the Law,
used to sit thus.

He, after he had conned all the mysteries
of natural philosophy and human history,
himself fulfilled Nature's decree,
Let compounds be dissolved,
In the year of Our Lord 1626,
of his age 66.

Thomas Meautys,
who loved him in life
and admires him in death,
set up this memorial
to this Great Man.

Index

Adamson, *Francis Bacon,* 178
Addison, Joseph, 158
Agricola, *De Re Metallica,* 10, 11-12, 26
Alembert, d', *Encyclopédie,* 137, 138
Anderson, *Philosophy of Francis Bacon,* 61, 78, 177-78
Andrewes, Bishop Lancelot, 73-74
Aquinas, Thomas, 27, 38
Aristotle, 11, 27, 93-94, 101, 151, 175
  History of Animals, 94
  Metaphysics, 67
artillery, 9, 10 (*see also* gunpowder)
Arundel, Lord, 167
astronomy, 39-40
Atomism, 177

Bacon, Anthony, 20, 22
Bacon, Francis:
  parentage and birth, 19-22; to court as a boy, 63; at Cambridge, 23, 27; earliest acquaintance with industries, 25-27; at Gray's Inn, 22, 30; at the French court, 14-15, 30-31; in Parliament, 32, 47-48; prosecutes Essex, 51-52
  marriage, 70-71; public career, 32, 57-58, 71, 72, 82, 155-59; solicitor-generalship, 57, 71;

Bacon, Francis (*Continued*)
  other offices and peerage, 82, 155; acceptance of bribes, 155-57, 159; trial and judgment, 157-58; imprisonment, 158; will, 71, 158; last writings, 159-60; illness and death, 166-67; condition of his writings at his death, 171-72
  his ambition, 5-6, 30, 32-33 (*see also below,* science, its practical application); his thirst for universal knowledge, 44; his own estimate of his character, 53-56, 116 (*see also under* Writings: letter to Lord Burghley); his logical method, 114-19; his use of Latin and English, 61, 62-63, 71-72, 77, 160; his vocabulary, 164-65; his style, 47, 83; financial affairs, 31-32, 51, 58, 155-57, 159

  OPINIONS AND DOCTRINES

  Agricola, *De Re Metallica,* 12
  alchemists, 34
  alphabet, the, 122
  Aristotle, 23-24, 27, 64-67, 93-94, 107, 146-47
  artillery, 34
  astronomy, 39

197

Bacon, Francis (*Continued*)
"Bensalem" in the *New Atlantis,*
117, 146
Bible, the, 146, 169, 170
Biringuccio, *Pirotechnia,* 12, 27
Church, Fathers of the, 107
commericum mentis et rei, 7
compass, magnetic, 6, 34, 42, 44
Copernicus, 39, 40
Creation, date of the, 75
deduction, 101
Democritus, 79, 130
England, 151
experimenta lucifera and *fructifera,* 110-12
experimental method, 92-93, 110,
111
Fall of Man, 146, 148-49
Four Idols, doctrine of the, 102-
103
Galileo, 130
geographical discoveries, 40-43
Gilbert, William, 42
good, the private and the common, 165-66
grammar, philosophical, 164
Greek philosophers, 23-24, 27,
34, 38, 63, 64-69, 74, 96-97,
104-105, 107, 146-47, 163,
177
gunpowder, 6, 8, 34, 44
Hammond, John, 154
Harvey, William, 154
heat and cold, 123-25, 167
human soul, 169-70
Idols of the Cave, etc., *see above,*
Four Idols
induction, 45, 101, 114-16
instances, *see* Prerogative Instances
instauratio defined, 75, 86, 146
inventions and discoveries, 6-10,
34, 44, 54, 111-12
knowledge, divine and natural,
169
language, 122, 164
"latent configuration" and "latent
process," 122, 130, 144

Bacon, Francis (*Continued*)
learning, history of, 163, 169
"literate experience," 110-11,
121, 162
Lucretius, 46
magnetism, *see* compass, magnetic
medieval philosophy, *see* Scholasticism
metallurgy and mining, 10, 12, 27
"metaphysics," 164
monopolies, 48
mythology, 76-77
nature, man's mastery over, *see*
science, its practical application
Paddy, Sir William, 154
Paracelsus, 100
philosophy, ancient, *see* Greek
philosophers *and* Scholasticism
philosophy, speculative and practical, 75
philosophy's relation to useful
crafts, *see* science, its practical application
Plato, 64-67, 147, 164
Pliny, 76, 167-68
poetry, 163
Prerogative Instances, doctrine
of, 128-31
printing, 6, 34, 42, 44
Reformation, the, 145
religion, views on, 5, 29, 46-47,
74, 75, 146-50, 169
Scholasticism, 27, 38, 59, 74, 107
science, its practical application
to man's needs, 3-4, 7-8, 10,
14-15, 16, 24, 30, 34-36,
44-45, 54, 60, 67-69, 94, 98-
99, 121
sciences, corruption of the—signs
of, 104-106; causes of, 106-
108; grounds for hope, 108-
10
"Solomon's House" in the *New
Atlantis,* 17, 35-36, 118, 146
spelling, phonetic, 164

Bacon, Francis (*Continued*)
State, supremacy of the, 47, 169
tillage replaced by pasture, 48
truth, 45, 142-43, 169
weights and measures, 48
works not yet written by anyone,
but needed, 161-64
writing, 110-11

WRITINGS

The Advancement of Learning,
58, 59-61, 71, 72, 73, 90,
160, 171
Book II, *De Augmentis Scientiarum,* 12, 39, 41-42, 59,
83, 90, 95, 147-48, 160-66,
168, 171; plan, 161-62
Arguments of Law, 83-84
autobiographical writing, only,
53-56
Cogitata et Visa, 62, 63-64, 67-
69, 71, 72, 86, 98, 144, 152,
172
Cogitationes de Humana Scientia,
61
Cogitationes de Natura Rerum,
61
*Concerning the Interpretation of
Nature,* see *De Interpreta-
tione Naturae*
De Augmentis Scientiarum, see
under *The Advancement of
Learning*
De Interpretatione Naturae, 62,
97; Preface, 53
De Sapientia Veterum, 71, 76-82,
171
Atalanta, 79-80
Cupid, 78-79
Daedalus, 79
Diomedes, 80-81
Prometheus, 81-82
Descriptio Globi Intellectualis,
62
*Description of the Intellectual
World,* see entry above
"devices," 33, 37, 38

Bacon, Francis (*Continued*)
*Encyclopedia of Nature and of
Art,* see under *The Great
Instauration*
Essays, 49-50, 58, 82, 166, 171
fables, see *De Sapientia Veterum*
Filum Labyrinthi, 62
The Forerunners, see under *The
Great Instauration*
The Great Instauration, 25, 30,
33, 56, 71, 73, 76, 82, 85-
140, 153, 155, 160, 171,
173, 175-76; Preface, 86,
88-89; plan, 89-91
Part 1, *The Division of the
Sciences,* 160
Part 2, *Novum Organum
(New Logic),* 6, 7, 14, 25,
67, 71, 90; Book I, 45, 86,
92-113, 114, 152, 171,
172; Book II, 114-31, 146,
171, 175-76
Part 3, *Encyclopedia of
Nature and of Art* (incl.
Parasceve and *List of
Particular Enquiries),* 90,
132-40, 146, 152, 159,
166, 172
Part 4, *The Ladder of the
Intellect,* 90
Part 5, *The Forerunners (Anticipations of the New Philosophy),* 90-91
Part 6, *The New Philosophy,*
91
The Greatest Birth of Time, see
Temporis Partus Maximus
History of Henry VII, 159
History of the Winds, 85, 148,
150, 159-60
The Ladder of the Intellect, see
under *The Great Instaura-
tion*
legal writings, 82-84
letter to Lord Burghley, 32-33,
34 n., 37, 38, 44
List of Particular Enquiries, see

Bacon, Francis (*Continued*)
 under *The Great Instauration*
Magnalia Naturae, 61
The Masculine Birth of Time, see *Temporis Partus Masculus*
The Mighty Works of Nature, see *Magnalia Naturae*
Mr. Bacon in Praise of Learning, 33-35, 37, 85
New Atlantis, 17, 36, 70, 89, 117-18, 146, 172
The New Logic (Novum Organum), see under *The Great Instauration*
The New Philosophy, see under *The Great Instauration*
Novum Organum, see under *The Great Instauration*
Of Unity in Religion, 46-47
On the Interpretation of Nature, see *De Interpretatione Naturae*
On the Wisdom of the Ancients, see *De Sapientia Veterum*
Parasceve, see under *The Great Instauration*
Phaenomena Universi, 62
The Phenomena of the Universe, see entry above
"philosopher's address," *see entry below*
Redargutio Philosophiarum, 30-31, 62, 65, 66, 70, 72, 147; "philosopher's address," 31, 70
Refutation of Philosophers, see entry above
Sacred Meditations, 146-48
speeches in Parliament, 48
Sylva Sylvarum (intended for the *Encyclopedia*), 172
Temporis Partus Masculus, 62, 64, 66, 147, 149
Temporis Partus Maximus, 29
Thema Coeli, 62
Theory of the Heavens, see entry above

Bacon, Francis (*Continued*)
Thoughts and Conclusions, see *Cogitata et Visa*
Thoughts on Human Knowledge, see *Cogitationes de Humana Scientia*
Thoughts on the Nature of Things, see *Cogitationes de Natura Rerum*
The Thread of the Labyrinth, see *Filum Labyrinthi*
The True Greatness of Britain, 151
Valerius Terminus, 60, 61, 80, 142
Bacon, Lady Francis (Alice Barnham), 70-71
Bacon, Sir Nicholas, 19-20, 23, 25, 26, 29, 31; verses to his wife, 20-21
Bacon, Lady Nicholas (Anne Cook), 20, 21-22, 25, 28, 33, 35; translation of Jewel's *Defence of the English Church*, 20, 21, 28
Baconian scholarship, history of, 171-78
Barnham, Alice, *see* Bacon, Lady Francis
Bible, the, 5, 74, 86, 145-46
Birch edition of Bacon, 173
Biringuccio, *Pirotechnia*, 10-11, 12, 26, 27, 84
Black, Joseph, 123
Blackbourne edition of Bacon, 25, 173
Bodin, Jean, 11
Boerhaave, Hermann, 153, 160 n.
Boswell, Sir William, 172
Brewer edition of Bacon, 176
Broad, *The Philosophy of Francis Bacon*, 177
Buckingham, Marquis of, 156, 157
Bury St. Edmunds abbey, 20
Bushell, Thomas, 10, 12

Caesar, *Commentaries*, 63
Calvin and Calvinism, 22, 25, 27-29, 47

Cambridge University, 20, 23, 36, 50, 168, 173
Charles I, 13
Charles II, 17
Childe, *Man Makes Himself,* 110
Church of England, 28, 74
Coke, Sir Edward, 57
Coleridge, *The Friend,* 137-38
Comenius, J. A., 17
compass, magnetic, 9, 44
Cook, Anne, *see* Bacon, Lady Nicholas
Cook, Sir Anthony, 20
Copernicus, *The Revolutions of the Heavenly Bodies,* 39-40
Cowley, *Ode to the Royal Society,* 17, 68
Cranmer, Thomas, 80
Creation, date of the, 75

Descartes, René, 15-16, 174
Diderot, *Encyclopédie,* 137, 138
dissolution of the monasteries, 13, 19, 20, 25, 151
Drake, Sir Francis, 41

Eden, *The Decades of the New World,* 26
elements, the four, 100, 123, 139
Elizabeth, Queen, 12, 17, 21, 23, 32, 33, 41, 43, 46, 50-52, 57, 71
Ellis, R. L., 83, 96, 173, 177
England—manufactures and industries, 13, 26-27; religious situation, 46-47
Essex, 2d Earl of, 33, 50-52, 58
Eton College, 158
experimental method, 93

Fleming, Sergeant Thomas, 58
Fowler edition of Bacon, 98, 176, 178
France—industrial progress, 13-14; scientific movement, 30-31; religious wars, 46
Frobisher, Sir Martin, 41

geographical discoveries, 9, 40-43
Gorhambury house, 25-26
Gough, *The Superlative Prodigal,* 12
Gray's Inn, 30, 83, 166; revels, 35
Gruter, Isaac, 172
gunpowder, 8-9, 10
Gunpowder Plot, 47

Hakluyt, Richard, 42-43
Harrison, *Bacon, Hobbes, Boyle . . . ,* 177
Hartlib, Samuel, 17
Harvey, William, 153-54, 175
Heath, D. D., 83, 173
Hegel, G. W. F., 37
Henry VIII, 13, 19
Henry the Navigator, Prince, 40
Herbert, *Elixir,* 29
Hicks, Sir Michael, 22
Hobbes, Thomas, 169
Hooke, *General Scheme . . . ,* 137
Hoover, Herbert and Lou Henry, 11 n.

industrial revolution, first, 12-13, 151

James I, 16, 17, 53, 58, 60, 71, 72, 87, 153, 158, 166
Jewel, Bishop John, 28; *Apologia,* 20, 21, 28

Kitchin edition of Bacon, 176
knowledge, how developed since Bacon's time, 170-71

Latimer, Hugh, 80
Laws and Statutes of Geneva, 28
Leibnitz, G. W. von, 177
Leicester, 1st Earl of, 50-51
life, the contemplative *vs.* the active, 27
Lucretius, 26

Macaulay, *Essay on Bacon,* 174, 176
Marx, *Capital,* 174-75

Mary, Queen, 28
Matthews, Sir Tobie, 47
Merton, *Science in Seventeenth Century England*, 27-28, 175
metallurgy and mining, 10-12, 13, 26
Mill, John Stuart, 175
Milton, John, 17
  Areopagitica, 146
  Of Reformation in England, 145
Montagu edition of Bacon, 173

Nef, *Industry and Government in France and England*, 175
Newton, Sir Isaac, 39

Osorius, Bishop, 41
Owen, Robert, 103
Oxford University, 42

Palissy, Bernard, 13-14, 15
  Discours Admirables, 14, 26
Parliament, 19, 32, 48, 156, 157-58
Paulet, Sir Amias, 30
philosophy, speculative and practical, 15-16
Plato, 177
  The Republic, 102
Pliny, *Natural History*, 11, 126, 138
printing, 8, 9
Ptolemy, Claudius, 39, 40
Puritans and Puritanism, 22, 28, 47

Raleigh, Sir Walter, 41, 43, 75
  History of the World, 75
Rawley, Dr. William, 23, 172, 174
  Life of Bacon, 23, 51, 85
religious beliefs in Bacon's day, 74-75

Ridley, Nicholas, 80
Roman Catholic Church, 47, 160
Royal Society, 17-18, 28, 74, 137

Scholasticism and the Schoolmen, 5, 30, 59, 151
Selden, John, 145
Shelley, Percy Bysshe, 24
ships, construction of, 9
Smyth, Sir Thomas, 12
Spedding, James, 24, 51, 53, 77-78, 173, 177
  The Letters and the Life, 174
  The Life and Times of Lord Bacon, 178
Spedding, Ellis, and Heath edition of Bacon, 83, 173, 177 n.
Sprat, Bishop Thomas, 18
Star Chamber, 32, 57
Stevin, Simon, 9
Sturt, *Francis Bacon*, 178

Taylor, *Francis Bacon*, 177
Tenison, Dr. Thomas, 77, 87
  Baconiana, 173

Ussher, Archbishop James, 75

Vico, Giovanni Battista, 63

Welch, *Europe's Discovery of South Africa*, 40 n.
Whitehorn, *Certain Waies for the Ordering of Souldiers in battelray*, 26
Wyclif, John, 145

York House, London, 20